Yellow Lights

Sean McKeveny

· · · · ● · ● · · ·

To my wife and three children,

Your love fills me daily.

Let us bring the world a greater appreciation for the Yellow Lights in life.

ONE

· • • ● • ● • • ·

LIGHT TAPS TURNED TO a persistent knock on the driver's side window.

"Wake up!"

Carter Wilson snapped his head off the steering wheel, rubbed his bloodshot eyes, and strained his cheeks with a fake smile as he turned to his family standing outside.

Carter had arrived early at his son James' school for the Fall Art Festival and had fallen asleep in the parking lot. After learning about his work colleagues missing a committed product release, Carter was still recovering from the cross-country, redeye two days earlier with M.E.Z.'s largest client.

Carter stepped out of his Jeep and kissed his wife, Emily, as their three-year-old Amelia snuck between her parents, now latched onto Carter's leg like a koala.

As the Wilson's walked towards the side entrance of the elementary school's gymnasium, James noticed his teacher standing at the doorway, ran up, and hugged her. With Halloween only a few weeks away, pumpkins and scarecrows lined the walkway into the gymnasium.

Carter shook hands with a few other parents outside before entering the gym packed with fall art projects that all the students had created.

James had started first grade just a couple of months before. Like many boys his age, James was in a dinosaur craze and his three-fold display included paintings of a t-rex, a raptor, an apatosaurus, and on the table in front of the display, a paper machete mold of a triceratops. Clipped to the upper-right of the display was a photo of James, smiling ear-to-ear.

The P.T.O. had arranged for screen prints of the artwork to be available to order on t-shirts, coffee mugs, and key chains. Half the money would go towards the new playground being built in the spring.

As Carter looked at James' display, James described why the eyes of one T-rex drawing were out of place.

"Daddy, this one is abstract art!" James said, pointing excitedly.

Amelia was already on the move to the other side of the gym, where it looked like a wild rave of children bouncing up and down to the Kidz Bop songs playing through the speakers.

James chased after his little sister, as Carter peered on like a hawk and Emily ventured to the P.T.O. table checking out different purchase options. After an hour or so at the school, Carter helped Emily load the kids into the S.U.V. and he hopped in his Jeep, offering to grab Chinese food on the way home.

Carter filled the next hour with family time before checking his work emails to see if there was any update from his thank you note following the cross-country trip earlier in the week. Carter sat in the den exhausted, shouted up the stairs 'Goodnight!', and fell asleep on the couch, with anticipation for the update meeting requested by his boss the next morning.

Carter's alarm sounded at 4:43 a.m. Carter tip-toed upstairs to his bedroom, attempting to not wake the family or cause the dog to bark. He pulled his work clothes from the closet, brought them into the bathroom, and showered quickly. As Carter got out of the shower, he noticed a t-shirt hanging behind the door with the abstract t-rex that James showed him the night before. There was also a handwritten sticky note attached.

"Good luck today! We love you. -Em"

Carter threw his undershirt to the side and decided to wear the t-rex shirt under his light blue dress shirt and navy-blue suit jacket.

Then, he went back through his bedroom, stumbled on clothes from the day prior, and banged his knee on the partially open dresser drawer.

Carter continued to tiptoe as he passed James and Amelia's bedrooms and went downstairs. As he entered the kitchen, he snagged a breakfast bar and hit the automatic start for the Jeep in the driveway. The family's chocolate lab, Zeus, whimpered at his crate. Carter let Zeus out, refilled the water bowl, and let the dog into the backyard.

After struggling to find a clean travel mug, Carter chose the one in the sink that he used the day before. He filled the mug with Nescafe grounds and proceeded with filtered water and ice from the refrigerator. Zeus, now standing at the back sliding door, barked once as Carter turned towards the garage to leave.

Carter's mind was already spinning as he turned to let Zeus back in, pulling the dog back to the crate.

As Carter stepped into the garage and opened the door to head to the driveway, he paused as the brisk fall air gave him goosebumps and he shifted his coat selection.

Despite the few minutes of the vehicle running while coffee was made and Zeus did his business out back, the windows remained fogged up. Carter slid the frost off the handle of the door before looking down the driveway to make sure he hadn't forgotten to bring the garbage out for Friday pick-up.

As the door opened, the radio started and the news of the city and stock market kicked the day into gear. Carter threw the car into reverse, cranked the defrost setting to the highest gear, and hit the automatic garage door button overhead.

Once out of the driveway and sitting on Colts Court, Carter hit for the antifreeze to spray the windshield while cold air continued gusting out of the air vents.

This is what he did for years, knowing that after being out of the neighborhood and driving on autopilot, everything would be clear.

The trip to the M.E.Z. office was about forty-five minutes and Carter knew he would arrive about two hours before any of his co-workers would get there. He considered the morning his time and the time when he was most productive. It was his time to zone in and plan the entire day. With a 10:00 a.m. meeting with his boss, Carter's focus this morning was more important than ever.

It was about 5:15 a.m. as Carter turned out of the neighborhood, just a mere thirty minutes or so after his alarm had gone off.

With a majority of the town still fast asleep, the traffic lights were set to a nighttime cadence of flashing reds and yellows. With the 5:15 a.m. routine being the norm, Carter had mapped out the way to slow roll every intersection, saving a few minutes on the commute in.

As he made his way through town, he passed the industrial park that was once the headquarters of a large Fortune 500 company. The history and roots of the town remained grounded in the golden age of 40,000+ jobs available to folks of all backgrounds. That industrial park was dark now and the footprint of the Fortune 500 company had shrunk to less than 2,000 local jobs. That company was what brought Carter's father to the area after completing his engineering degree and what provided about three generations in the area a wonderful middle-class life, funded mostly by the great jobs and opportunities that came with the Fortune 500 company.

The travel coffee mug sat in the closest cup holder, M.E.Z. company logo engraved. In the mug was the iced coffee, giving Carter an extra jolt to his morning routine for years. Normally the twenty-ounce cup lasted the ride and through the clean-up of urgent emails during the first thirty minutes in the office.

Carter took a swig as he approached the middle of town. A flashing yellow light sat in the middle of the town. Ahead was Town Hall and the Court House and to the right, a large flagpole and war memorials. The intersection of Washington Avenue and Center Street was desolate. The local convenience store owner was just lighting the Open sign of the store and the banner for the Halloween Parade was lit up and sashed across the front of the Town Hall building.

The weather news had just finished as Carter approached the flashing yellow. The cross traffic had a flashing red. It was 5:23 a.m. and Carter Wilson was already settling into the morning commute.

Just ahead of the main intersection was a small plaza with a barbershop, Subway, nail salon, and pharmacy. The entrance to the interstate was about a mile ahead with a yellow light before the right turn onto the ramp.

The ramp to the interstate was about a quarter mile long and downhill, allowing the merge onto the seventy-mile-per-hour expressway to happen with ease.

But it didn't happen with ease for Carter. The eighteen-wheeler alongside had no opportunity to stop and the company logoed coffee cup of iced coffee hit the windshield, followed by the Jeep flipping and the daily rush coming to a halted stop.

Sharp beeping sounds and a squeeze of his right hand were Carter's first sensations as he opened his eyes. The brightness of lights blinded Carter as his eyelids peeked slowly open as swelling kept the left eye open only a sliver.

Carter recognized the ring of the person holding his hand. It was his wife, Emily.

··········

Emily was something special and the first girl Carter loved. They met each other right out of undergrad while Carter was traveling.

Emily's green eyes caught Carter's piercing blue ones from across the coffee shop and her "don't mess with me" vibe attracted Carter, who was always someone looking for a challenge.

The beauty of her jet-black hair and green eyes entranced Carter. Emily's beauty was enhanced by her intelligence and family values Carter learned about the first night they met.

After reluctantly agreeing to give Carter her number as she was reading her book in the coffee shop, the two talked for an hour or so before Emily took off to pick up her sister

Carter knew after just a few hours of meeting Emily that she was unlike any other woman he had ever met. As Carter returned to visit the city where Emily was making her career, they would go on dates and eventually

Emily made a trip to visit Carter who was living states away. Emily and Carter both had early career success and were standing out as leaders in their respective organizations.

After weekend trips for close to six months, Emily and Carter reached a point where they were forced to have difficult conversations about what their relationship path forward would look like. Carter admittedly was someone who had always focused on having and getting what he wanted, and that meant persuading Emily to join him several states away, leaving a stable job, and taking a chance on love.

·····•·•·····

Emily's weekday alarm was set for 5:45 a.m., so the call from the E.M.S. at 5:42 a.m. was initially thought to be the alarm, so she dismissed it quickly for the standard eight-minute snooze. When the alarm sounded three minutes later, Emily looked at her phone to see a voicemail. Then looking at the caller ID, she trembled in fear previewing the nineteen-second transcript. "Emily Wilson, this is Officer Fisher, Carter is being rushed to Upstate Medical. Please call us back as soon as possible." Tears flooded Emily's eyes. The night prior she had just fought with Carter about not helping put the kids to bed and she had no idea what was happening. Fear consumed her and her heart raced as she sat on the edge of the bed, pausing before redialing the missed number.

Officer Fisher picked up on the first ring, "What's going on? Is Carter okay?" The Officer said he couldn't share all the details, but her husband had been in a serious accident and needed to be rushed to the hospital. Emily ran out of the bedroom and fell to her knees between James and Amelia's room. Tears flooded her face as she gasped for air and grabbed the banister to pull herself up. She opened Amelia's door first. Emily's sweet little girl slept peacefully as the sound machine drowned out the noise from Carter getting ready earlier and Emily sobbing moments before.

James' bedroom door was already open and he too was asleep.

Despite knowing very little about the severity of Carter's accident, Emily knew she needed to get to the hospital and fast.

Emily returned to her bedroom, threw on a sweatshirt and sweats, and headed downstairs as she called her mother-in-law.

"Emily...Is everything okay?" Gram Wilson asked.

Through tears and deep breaths, Emily replied, "No, it's not. I need to get to the hospital for Carter and need you here."

"Oh my god, oh my god. What happened?" Gram Wilson began her tailspin of emotions.

"He got in an accident and is being rushed to the hospital," Emily answered while sliding on her shoes and rushing into the garage.

Gram Wilson sobbed on her way to Carter's house, reliving the memories of her youngest son and the uncertainty about what was going on. Before Gram arrived, James woke up and made his way to the kitchen. The unlocking at the front door caused James to curl up on the couch under a blanket.

Gram walked into the kitchen as Zeus began barking.

James slid the blanket off his head and peered over the back of the couch, looking at his grandmother, still in pajamas and with a bright red face.

"Where is Mommy?" James asked. Gram ran and gave James a big hug, unable to immediately reply. Tears fell onto the shoulder of James' shirt.

Finally, after catching her breath, Gram said, "Mommy had to go help Daddy. He forgot something really important."

·· •·• ·••·· ·

Still groggy, Carter heard Emily say, "Carter...We love you. Everything will be okay." Carter felt a tear roll down his face, still unable to comprehend what happened or what was ahead. The doctor came into the room, seeing Carter was starting to come to and his first words were, "Pause, look around".

Yellow Light 1: Pause and look around.

Two

· · · • · • · · ·

A FULL TWENTY-FOUR HOURS had passed since the flipped Jeep settled perpendicular to the eighteen-wheeler that screeched to a halt. The expressway on-ramp remained closed for hours, causing thousands to be rerouted during their Friday morning commutes.

After the eighteen-wheeler hit the Jeep and the guardrail about a quarter mile ahead, the driver of the eighteen-wheeler noticed the lights of the overturned Jeep about 300 feet back. Before even getting out of the truck, the driver dialed 9-1-1 and was fortunate to hear from the dispatcher that a police officer was only a few miles away and starting en route.

A young patrolman on Officer Fisher's team was first to the scene. The patrolman was only five months into the job and guided to police work by the fact his father and brother were also on the force. The patrolman called for backup before even exiting his vehicle with nerves through the roof, knowing that what he was likely to see wasn't going to be pretty. The patrolman opened the glove compartment of his vehicle and thumbed to the overturned vehicle section of his training book to validate one item before opening the door and approaching the overturned Jeep.

As the patrolman shuffled between the broken glass, got down into an army crawl through a shattered window, and found Carter's wrist to check his pulse.

The E.M.S. team arrived and assessed the situation. The driver's side door was removed and the team focused on reducing blood loss and stabilizing Carter.

As they carried Carter's lifeless body to the ambulance, Officer Fisher arrived, passing by a few vehicles that had stopped alongside the accident. Additional emergency vehicles lined the on-ramp to the highway as the driver's side door was removed and Carter's limp body was carried off. Officer Fisher, now guiding additional officers to block the ramp and handle additional road closures and redirections, looked back to see Carter's mangled right leg being wrapped intensely. It was at that point Officer Fisher received Emily's contact information and left the heart-wrenching 5:42 a.m. voicemail.

Now in the hospital and at the Doctor's advice, Carter attempted to look around. Minor movements of his neck caused his head to throb and Emily continued stroking her husband's hair. The plastic wristband was Carter's first signal of where he could be and what might have happened.

Wilson, Carter, Male 34, Blood Type O, Organ Donor.

The hospital bed of the I.C.U. remained flat but his right leg was elevated with a contraption holding it stable. Carter turned his head a bit more to the right, grimacing in pain, now able to see his wife sitting with a chair pulled snug to the hospital bed. Through a face of exhaustion and tears, Emily's green eyes met Carter's.

Over Emily's right shoulder, taped to the wall were two drawings. One was from James and the other from Amelia. James' drawing had a dinosaur surrounded by a large heart. Amelia's four stick figures were taped to the right. The two big stick figures were in a teal crayon, one of the smaller was pink, the other green. Carter noticed his mother's writing on Amelia's drawing, "We love you!"

The strain of keeping his eyes open caused Carter to turn to a less straining position. As Carter stared at the tiled ceiling, the slates between the tiles showed reflections of blue and red lights from the machines behind the bed.

Carter's first words were, "How did I get here?"

A man appeared alongside Emily, placing his hand on her shoulder.

"Carter, you are at Upstate Medical. You just woke up. You were in a bad car accident and needed emergency surgery."

Each breath was a strain for Carter, but he pushed another sentence out, "Give me all the details."

This was one of the lines Emily was all too familiar with and one Carter's co-workers feared to be asked. Carter was someone who always wanted to know every detail possible, and he always thought with all of the details, he alone could figure out the right resolution.

It was clear the question threw the man off, as he pulled his hand off Emily's shoulder and took a step back.

Emily broke in. "Baby, on your way to work, your Jeep flipped. You just had major reconstructive surgery on your right leg, you broke some ribs, have eighty-plus stitches in various spots. You are lucky to be alive."

Carter's head tipped back slightly following this briefing from Emily. The reaction was not noticed by the man but it was a sign that Emily knew meant her husband was overwhelmed. It was the same tilt he would give in the evenings after the kids were down, they were attempting to watch T.V., and Carter's phone vibrated with another work email.

The man now still standing behind Emily finally introduced himself.

"I am Doctor Z, the Chief Physician here. Emily is right. When I saw you yesterday, I didn't expect I'd be having this conversation. When the ambulance arrived, your blood loss was concerning, and we weren't sure a transfusion and immediate emergency surgery was going to work as well as it did." Doctor Z shifted from behind Emily along the bed towards the front of the bed so that he could look Carter in the eyes.

"Understand that the simple fact you asked me 'How did I get here?' is beyond where I thought you would be. I will be making my way around the hospital but want you to know that while you are here, we will care for you and improve you beyond the injuries sustained."

Doctor Z came to Upstate Medical about thirty years ago after starting his medical career in Texas. Now in his early sixties, Doctor Z's days were spent as much on training and inspiring as leading and directing the medical actions of the team. Doctor Z's dark eyes with noticeable bags, were hidden behind bottomless framed glasses.

Carter did not respond as he closed his eyes and appeared to fall back asleep. While still slightly awake but groggy from the post-surgery medicines, Carter overheard some information shared with Emily.

"He seems like a strong and determined person. We will have to have a similar discussion tomorrow. It's unlikely he will remember much of this and I have a feeling his acceptance of what's ahead will be a big hurdle for all of us. He will need to know that self-acceptance proceeds transformation and recovery."

Emily nodded, both hands now holding her husband's.

Doctor Z called out to a nurse on the floor, "Anjali, can you please take Mrs. Wilson to get some breakfast?"

A young nurse arrived at the door. She had been off the prior two days and was about two hours into her twelve-hour shift. Her smile beamed as she arrived at the doorframe introducing herself to Emily.

"Good morning Mrs. Wilson. I'm Anjali. I know it's been a long and stressful twenty-four hours. The breakfast orders won't come around for another hour. Could you come with me and I will take you to the twenty-four-hour cafeteria?"

Anjali peered in from the doorway. She saw Emily's head down and Doctor Z standing in the front of the room. The twenty seconds of silence broke as Doctor Z tapped Emily on the shoulder.

"Emily, I would really like you to go with Anjali and step away for a few minutes."

Emily had been up the last twenty-four hours since she rushed out of the house and to the hospital. She hadn't stepped outside. It was more than twelve hours since Gram Wilson dropped off the drawings from the kids, a change of clothes for Emily, and an Italian sub. The hospital staff brought that bag up as Emily sat in the I.C.U. Surgery waiting area. More than food, Emily needed some fresh air and agreed to head down with Anjali.

Anjali walked past the center desk of the I.C.U. and let the other nurses behind the desk know that she was heading down to the cafeteria with Mrs. Wilson and asked if anyone needed anything.

"Can you grab me a salad?" an older nurse called from behind the computer screen.

Emily walked to the elevator with Anjali. "What floor is the cafeteria on and is there a door to the outside where I could get fresh air?"

"The cafeteria is just one floor down, but I am coming with you. It's locked right now to guests, but we can get in with my employee badge."

"I am fine on my own," Emily replied, so tired to even notice the elevator door had opened and that the employee badge would be needed.

"I insist! The team has everything on the floor under control." Anjali grabbed her hand and they stepped into the elevator.

Emily looked down, disgruntled to be touched but was too exhausted to argue. Although having little to no appetite, Emily knew she had to get food in her system and had no idea what the next twenty-four hours would look like.

Anjali used her badge to get into the back hallway leading to the cafeteria. The two women entered the main area of the cafeteria, where metal gates hung from the ceiling until 7:30 a.m.

"Hello Ms. Anjali," the older gentleman behind the food display said, as he looked to be preparing for the official daily opening of the cafeteria.

Emily grabbed a yogurt parfait and regular coffee while Anjali grabbed a salad for her colleague upstairs. "Ma'am, I hope you and your family have a blessed day."

As Anjali headed back towards the elevator and Emily took a detour, following a sign towards the Rose Garden.

It was still before 7:00 a.m. and the plant life that likely filled the garden just a month before was covered with October frost.

A few hours earlier, Emily learned that Carter would remain in the I.C.U. for at least three days, then be sent upstairs for a few more, and have months of physical therapy after leaving the hospital. The physical, mental, and emotional exhaustion she was feeling was going to extend for a long time.

After five minutes in the garden, Emily returned to the I.C.U. floor where her phone was vibrating. There were about twenty unread messages from friends, family, and her co-workers checking in. To add to the stress of the situation, Emily had just started a new job four months before and was needing to find backups for her shifts this week.

Carter's phone was destroyed in the crash and Emily was honestly happy about that. She felt like he was more connected to that than any other object, including herself. A coworker of Carter's, named Nancy, lived around the block and was able to relay the news to the rest of the company.

Emily drank her coffee and called her mother-in-law to check on the kids and to give a more detailed update.

Gram and Grandpa had offered to take James and Amelia to their house for the weekend and the dog, Zeus. They wanted to help however they could and knew that taking the kids and dog would alleviate some of the stress of Emily worrying about what was going on at home.

Emily finished the yogurt parfait and prayed next to her husband. Doctor Z popped back in to check the monitors and administer another dose of pain meds. He said, "Emily, he is now stable, I really would like you to go home and rest."

Doctor Z then noticed the drawings on the wall.

"I have a grandson named James. He's into cars right now. Again, Emily...please get some rest.

Doctor Z cleared the whiteboard on the wall ahead of Carter's bed and wrote in all capital letters, 'NOW'. Emily stared at the board confused. Doctor Z mentioned that tomorrow would be a big day.

Doctor Z sat on the stool looking at Emily, "Please go home. Trust me. He will be okay."

While she gathered her things, Doctor Z exited the I.C.U. room.

"Know that the self who begins this process, will not be the same that ends it."

Yellow Light 2: Understand what got you to this moment.

THREE

· • • ● • ● • ● • ·

EMILY RETURNED HOME TO an empty house. She pulled into the driveway of 11 Colts Court and saw an Amazon box and another package on the doorstep. She grabbed both items and entered the garage.

Carter's Specialized bike hung on the wall above the scooters and bikes belonging to James and Amelia. Emily had recently converted the back area of the garage into a makeshift mudroom, with seating, cubbies, a coat rack, and a shelf for hats.

Emily set the boxes on the bench and kicked her shoes off. One flew backward. She turned to grab the shoe which lay upside down next to the beach chairs purchased for a trip the family had scheduled around the holidays.

Emotionless, she placed the shoes in the cubby and ripped open the Amazon box and tossed it into the middle of the garage. She snagged the plastic bags inside containing the family's Halloween costumes, took the second box, and headed into the empty house.

Emily sat down at the kitchen table in absolute exhaustion. The table had six seats and was oval. Early in their relationship, Carter and Emily refinished the table that used to belong to Gram and Grandpa. Emily normally sat at the head of the table, closest to the kitchen.

Emily called Carter's parents to give them another update to let them know she was home.

"Hi Emily, how is Carter?" Gram asked as background noise flooded Emily's ear. "I just put you on speaker and the kids are here."

"Hi, Mom. I got home and am going to shower and nap."

"Darling, you must be so exhausted. The kids are right here."

"Hi, Mommy!" James yelled.

Grandpa Wilson was now standing by Gram listening in. Emily could hear Amelia and James fighting in the background about what to watch on TV.

After providing some updates from the doctors, Emily reminded Grandpa and Gram about the kids' soccer later that day. Emily continued the conversation while walking around the house, closing the blinds that were left open, and turning off the basement lights before setting the home alarm and heading upstairs.

Emily walked up the stairs of the center hall colonial, passing James and Amelia's bedrooms.

"Love you guys!" Emily ended the call before laying down on the king-size bed.

When she left the hospital a few hours earlier, an I.C.U. nurse mentioned tests that would be taking place around 10:00 a.m. that day.

Emily set her alarm for two hours, lay down, and fell asleep seconds later.

The same vibrating noise that came when Officer Fisher called started going off right next to Emily's pillow, startling her from a deep sleep. Fearing the worst, Emily's heart rate dropped when she saw it was just the alarm. After hitting the 'Stop' button and sitting up against the headboard, Emily navigated through the settings on her phone and changed the vibrate cadence to avoid future retriggers of the horrible early morning call.

She jumped in the shower, threw her hair in a bun, put on a sweatshirt and yoga pants, and was back in her car headed to the hospital. Emily parked in the I.C.U. guest parking spaces went through security, and onto the elevator. Doctor Z was ending his shift as she exited the elevator. She had missed the handoff to the new shift, but the tests had yet to start.

"Emily, how are you doing?" Doctor Z asked in a calm and sincere tone.

Emily replied, "Fine."

Another nurse was holding the door open, but Doctor Z motioned he would wait for the next one. He looked at Emily again, "How about I tell you how I am doing, and then I want you to answer with more than one word?"

Emily was agitated by the comment and just wanted to get to Carter.

"I learned early in Med School that a one-word response to 'How are you?' does not allow the person to truly express how they feel. I personally am stressed right now. My youngest daughter is overseas studying abroad, and she didn't text me or my wife yesterday. I tried to reach her through WhatsApp and saw she read the message. I know she's twenty-one and likely just sleeping off a late night with friends but there is always fear of your children's safety."

*I didn't ask you but okay...*Emily thought.

"Now again, Emily, how are you doing?"

Emily breathed deeply. "I am exhausted. I almost lost my husband. I know this recovery is going to put more strain on all of us and I need to see Carter."

Seeing growing tension, Doctor Z replied, "Go ahead. I will be in tomorrow and we will look to get Carter out of the I.C.U."

Emily made her way from the elevator area into the I.C.U. around the center desk. Anjali was there sitting down behind the desk.

"Hi, Emily; Carter has been sleeping but I will be coming in shortly to prepare for the x-ray and arterial Doppler exam to monitor the blood flow."

Emily entered I.C.U. Room 5. The I.C.U. had magnets outside of each room with either a red, yellow, or green magnet signifying the patient's status. Emily noticed Carter's had moved from red to yellow.

Carter's normally cleanshaven face now showed stubble and the bruises on his face appeared darker than even a few hours before.

Emily carried the second box that was made out to Carter under her arm and placed it on the windowsill. The outside of the box said 'Get Well Wishes' but there was no return label.

With Carter still asleep, Emily used her front door key to cut the tape sealing the box. Inside there was a small note, 'Carter – We wish you a speedy recovery. Richie and the M.E.Z. Team.'

Emily crumbled the note and removed some wax paper to find a fruit and chocolate basket. She grabbed the caramel-dipped pretzel and reset the basket against the window.

Anjali knocked and entered the room. Carter was still asleep.

Anjali asked if Emily wanted to try waking Carter. Emily stroked her husband's dirty-blonde hair away from his eyebrows and saw him slowly open his eyelids.

"Hi Emily, I love you and am sorry this happened," Carter said, looking into his wife's eyes.

Anjali gave the couple a moment, standing quietly behind. She had already introduced herself in the past but knew from experience that the medicines and recovery sometimes warranted reintroductions.

"Carter, my name is Anjali, I am your main I.C.U. nurse. I will be helping you today and tomorrow." She went to the whiteboard and wrote, 'Patience'.

"Today you will have a few more tests before we are able to have the doctors assess how the surgery went. We have to determine what else might be going on and hopefully, we can get you out of the I.C.U. and onto one of the main floors."

Anjali looked up at Carter and Emily. "I wrote patience because that will be the word of the day to live by."

Anjali then explained that the first three items were goals for the day and the following were priorities. To show Carter and Emily how it would work, she joined in sharing her own.

Anjali wrote under the goals, complete tests, then asked Carter, "What's your goal for the day?"

"Understand what's next," Carter replied.

Anjali wrote that on the board and then turned to Emily, "What's your goal for the day?"

"Do not fear the unknown." Emily shared.

Anjali continued writing that the priority she had was stability. She then mentioned that she wanted Carter and Emily to pick only one word and spoke of how goals and priorities can be very different but identifying a priority as one word makes it easier to stay on track. Carter chose health and Emily chose faith.

Anjali stepped away from the board and went towards the monitors. "I'll be back in a few and we will head out for those tests."

Emily shifted her chair alongside the bed, looking at Carter's leg and digesting the exercise they just completed with Anjali. She noticed a key distinction in Carter's eagerness to know what's next where she seemed to be turning more towards faith and trust in the unknown.

Carter also sat staring at the whiteboard and then noticed the basket on the windowsill. "Who sent that?"

"They are from Richie and the office."

Emily quickly noticed the monitors show an increase in Carter's heart rate.

Carter's mind shifted to a presentation that was scheduled for the following week.

"Did you happen to get my phone?" Carter asked.

Emily let go of his hand and stood up over him.

"ARE YOU FUCKING KIDDING ME?!!!! YOU'RE PHONE IS BROKEN. YOU ALMOST DIED."

Emily walked to the door and turned around before exiting.

"IF IT MAKES YOU FEEL BETTER, NANCY TOLD ME ALL YOUR EMAILS ARE BEING FORWARDED TO NATALIE."

Seeing Emily storm out, Carter knew he was in the wrong and also knew his inability to disconnect from work had been the root of several issues in recent weeks. Carter took a deep breath and punched the railing of the bed frustrated at the situation and himself.

Emily stood in the hallway with tears of anger rolling down her face. She noticed Anjali getting ready to head back in, so she reluctantly returned to the room.

"I am sorry!" Carter said. "But, can I ask you something?" Emily nodded, now looking up at her husband with puffy eyelids and tear-soaked cheeks. "If I were to have died, how would everyone live?"

A reply would have to wait, at that moment, Anjali returned ready to wheel Carter for an x-ray, and blood work. Following the reconstruction of his leg, it was important to see how everything looked.

The tests would happen on the other side of the hospital, so Anjali shifted a few wires from the monitors to allow the bed to be mobile.

Emily sat again in isolated frustration. She peered up again at the whiteboard as the question Carter asked replayed in her head. "If I were to have died..."

Fuck him. I have sacrificed so much. This situation is already awful and I am asked to think about how it could be worse.

A mix of frustration, exhaustion, and anger was jumbled with gratitude and hope.

Maybe this forced pause is the only way Carter's thick head will understand to let go.

Sitting and feeling each emotion, Emily finally chose to pray as the tests were underway on the other side of the hospital.

The tests lasted about an hour and Carter finally understood the severity of the situation as x-ray images were shown of his leg before the surgery. They were on file from two years back when he had terrible shin splints after a marathon.

Carter's right leg now looked to be in bionic form with rods and screws. The x-ray technician, not with the best bedside manner said, "I imagine six months of physical therapy?"

Carter didn't know how to digest the reality that for six months his life was going to be significantly different, little did he know the differences experienced in that time would extend far beyond just the initial rehab period.

As Carter returned to the room, Emily pulled over the tray of food that had been delivered. Anjali hooked the machines back up to the wall and let

Emily and Carter know that Doctor Z would run through the test results with them when he got back the next day.

"Hopefully we can aim to get you out of the I.C.U. tomorrow." Anjali mentioned before leaving the room.

Emily and Carter ate the grilled cheese sandwiches and FaceTimed their kids.

"Daddy, I heard you are like Iron Man now," James said. "I went pee pee in Gram's potty today" Amelia yelled in the background.

"I miss you guys. Daddy is okay and we will see you soon." Emily smiled before ending the FaceTime session.

Although it was only Saturday, Emily knew Gram and Grandpa would need to help next week and the Sunday routine of getting everything mapped out for the week would fall onto someone else's shoulders.

Emily stayed at the hospital late that night, watching H.G.T.V. with Carter.

"Do you remember when we grabbed that dresser off the side of the road for the first apartment?" Carter asked.

"Oh my gosh, yes. I wish we had kept that with us when we moved back." Emily replied. "I sanded that thing down when I was pregnant with James, then I had to have you whitewash it and I bought those stupid lion-head knobs."

"It was perfect for the guest room. We should get back into that stuff" Carter said, turning to his wife.

Emily laughed at the memory. "Well, we've been talking about finishing the basement since we moved in. That would be a big project we could try to tackle." After the last episode of Love It or List It, Carter suggested Emily head home to get a good night's rest.

"I have not asked you, how are you doing Emily?"

Carter always had a problem with spewing his problems and emotions out to Emily but rarely took the time to hear or listen to hers.

Emily paused at the question. She knew a one-word answer was not appropriate and the mixed emotions she was feeling were fully aired out.

"I am grateful you are alive and I love you. I am exhausted because even before all of this happened, I was running on fumes managing everything with the kids, getting settled in my new job, and feeling like nothing I did was ever enough for you."

Carter looked at his wife and knew there was more she had to say.

"You move at a million miles an hour and aren't patient. Even when we were told the results of the tests wouldn't be shared until Doctor Z came back, I could sense your frustration.

I don't know why you asked about what I felt about if you were to have died. That didn't happen and thankfully it didn't. What we are dealing with right now is bad enough. You need to take this moment to reset on many fronts. I do love you and will always love you. Just know that I am doing all that I can and I want you to look up at that board and see how I am pushing to trust the unknown when you are continuously planning and wanting to know the next step. Stop taking the little things for granted tomorrow is not a guarantee. Turn back to trusting you will control what you can control and attempting to control things out of your control will only lead to frustrations."

Emily stopped and hugged Carter.

Carter whispered in her ear, "I needed to hear that more than you know. You are and forever will be my rock. I promise to do everything in my control to come out of this whole experience a better husband, father, and man."

Emily gave Carter a long kiss and headed home.

Yellow Light 3: Show you care by not allowing others to share only one-word responses.

FOUR

· · · · · ● · ● · · · ·

CARTER'S NORMAL EARLY MORNING wake-up was pushed back a bit but he was still a few hours into SportsCenter when Emily arrived.

"Good morning. Your dad dropped this on the porch yesterday to bring to you." Emily kissed Carter on the head and handed him a word search book.

Book in hand, Carter said, "So the x-ray technician mentioned six months of physical therapy."

Yeah, dummy, you shattered your leg. Did you think you were going to be running around tomorrow?

Emily figured it was going to be longer.

"We will do what we need to do," Emily replied as she got settled in.

Doctor Z greeted the staff at the I.C.U. center desk.

Anjali was on her 7:00 a.m.- 7:00 p.m. shift and a few hours in. She had already been in to see Carter before Emily arrived.

Carter and Emily talked about the kids and the week ahead.

"Oh shoot, I forgot I need to call Kate to see if she can get the kids off the bus. Your parents have an appointment." Emily grabbed her phone and called their neighbor.

As Emily was on the phone, Carter sat in the bed watching Doctor Z bring the entire team together, each taking turns to share updates on the patients. He then went to the whiteboard in the middle and wrote one word 'HONESTY' in all caps on a grid similar to what Anjali walked him and Emily through yesterday. Doctor Z then allowed the head nurse and a med school resident set the goals and priorities for the day.

Carter saw Doctor Z leave the morning round-up and head to a room across the hall.

"I saw Doctor Z was here, I know I might be more stable than other people on the floor but why wouldn't he come in here and give me an update on the results?" Carter said this aloud, Emily only caught the tail-end, as she was wrapping up the call with Kate.

"Carter, remember the word that's on that board," Emily said, directing her husband's attention to be more patient.

Carter was right that he was more stable than others, and now had a green magnet on his door. Being the most stable, it wasn't until about noon before Doctor Z finally entered Carter's room.

"I am sorry for the delay; we had two patients come in last night that I pray make it through today, and I heard from Anjali that you were doing well."

Carter, in his best attempt to show he was following the word of the prior day, gave a nod. "Anjali asked me to be patient but obviously I am eager to get out of the I.C.U. today if possible."

Discounting that Carter was still not being patient, Doctor Z replied, "Understood." Now turning towards Emily, "How are you?"

Emily knew from the prior elevator interaction that 'Fine' would not do.

"I am relieved Carter will be out of the I.C.U. soon and look forward to hearing more about the results and your recovery plan."

Doctor Z smiled as he saw Emily standing at the front of the room in front of the whiteboard Anjali filled out with the Wilsons yesterday.

"I see Anjali introduced you to W.P.G." Both Carter and Emily looked puzzled.

Doctor Z clarified the confusion. "Sorry, word, priorities, goals. The prior Doctor I took over for implemented this concept years ago." He went on to explain.

"Having a single word serves as your compass for the day. It seems like 'patience' was yesterday's word and it seems like we still have some work to do." Doctor Z stared humorously at Emily. "It also looks like you hope to 'understand what's next.'"

Doctor Z then grabbed the whiteboard eraser and cleared the details from yesterday. While erasing the board, a beaded bracelet with Papa was exposed, as the sleeve of his lab coat shifted down his forearm.

"Today, our word will be 'HONESTY'. I am going to have to tell you some tough stuff today and it's important we both reciprocate honesty in our emotions and words."

Carter and Emily were then asked about their goals and priorities. Carter's goal: 'Get out of the I.C.U.' and the one-word priority, 'clarity'.

Doctor Z pulled a tablet off the rolling cart. Anjali was now standing in the doorway. Doctor Z always looked to ensure his message was heard clearly by other staff members involved with the treatment plan. Doctor Z began to give his summary of the test results.

"The surgeons did an amazing job on your leg. Everything appears to be in the right place and most importantly the blood flow seems to be getting better." It wasn't until that moment Carter noticed his leg had been lowered a bit in the night. "I do have some concerns about the bruising around the stitches behind your leg. We are going to need to monitor that closely in the days ahead. Later today, I will do everything in my power to get you onto a main floor. It's likely to be another week or so here and then you'll focus on transitioning back to home under a rehab plan put together by our P.T. staff."

The word home brought warmth to Emily's heart. Just days prior when she arrived and was told Carter was in emergency surgery with severe blood loss, the idea of what Carter's return home would look like was unknown.

"Can I get some sort of documentation of the plan?" Carter asked in his executive voice. "I do better visually, seeing things mapped." Seeing the eyebrows dip down on Doctor Z's face and a side-to-side shake of the head with an eye roll, Carter continued. "You know, so I can know what I can control and we can stick to that plan."

Doctor Z looked up and met eyes with Emily before shifting to Carter. "Mr. Wilson, your recovery does not have an instruction manual. There is no step-by-step guide that any logical medical professional can give to a patient who just experienced the trauma you did."

Emily and Anjali now locked eyes. Emily had overheard too many of Carter's similar requests to co-workers and the blowouts that followed.

Carter took a deep audible breath, realizing some of the venting from Emily last night was directly tied to Carter's normal responses in situations like this.

"Understood. Let's just focus on the day." Carter said with a sideways look to Emily to see if she recognized his changed approach.

Not addressing Carter's request, Doctor Z left the room. "I will be back shortly." Anjali remained in the doorway planning to take a look at the monitors. Carter looked at Emily,

"Hey, I am trying."

"I saw the shift babe but I am just too emotionally stretched to deal with you needing to be in control of what expert doctors and nurses know they need to do," Emily replied.

Emily noticed Anjali was still in the doorway but appeared to be talking to Doctor Z who was now out of sight.

After about thirty seconds, filled only by the beeping of the I.C.U. machines, a staff member came in for Carter's lunch order.

"Would you like anything?" the worker asked Emily.

"I'm okay, I am going to just head downstairs and grab a coffee." Emily needed a break.

Emily headed to the elevator and down to the cafeteria she visited before. It was now open to staff and guests.

"Hello Ma'am" greeted the older gentleman. "If you see Doctor Z, tell him we have his favorite sub for lunch today."

Yellow Light 4: There is no step-by-step guide to life.

FIVE

· · • · • · • · ·

As EMILY RETURNED TO the I.C.U., Doctor Z was sitting with the team at the center desk and called out. "Emily, they are getting a spot in the hospital open. Anjali will be there soon."

Emily, now heading down the hall yelled back, "Sounds good. The guy in the cafeteria told me to tell you they have your favorite sub today."

Doctor Z laughed. "I can't say no to a good buffalo chicken sub."

Emily continued past Rooms 1 and 3 on her way to Room 5 where Carter was now watching the news. The cleaning crew was turning Room 1. The night prior, a heart attack victim passed away from a second attack. She did not know but Carter knew those details as he was woken up in the middle of the night to the curdling crying of the victim's loved ones two rooms down.

The physical closeness to death and those in critical care was something new to Carter.

Anjali came to Carter's room. She was working a double and was involved with the death overnight. Alongside her was a man in a medical jacket. Anjali introduced him, "This is Justin. He is in his last year of med school and doing his residency here."

Justin had the frame of a linebacker, with his left ear a bit swollen, as if he may have been a wrestler. "Hello, Mr. & Mrs. Wilson. I will be helping Anjali with the transfer."

Anjali took Carter's vitals and Emily continued sipping her coffee and asked in a friendly manner, "So after residency, what area do you want to focus on?"

Justin, who had been intently watching Anjali go through the vitals and wire transition from the wall to the mobile version answered. "I want to focus on mental health. Still unsure of any specialization."

Carter saw a rubber band around Justin's wrist. It was very popular in the community about eight years back. The royal blue band was for a non-profit started after a local high school quarterback committed suicide a week before the state championship.

Carter and Emily had not been living around the area at the time of the tragedy but Carter was following the success of his former high school football team that year and recently attended the memorial walk honoring Kyle Zito. Kyle wore the same jersey number that Carter did and it was retired by the school, so Carter was familiar with the whole story.

Pointing to the band, "Did Kyle spark your interest?"

Yeah, Kyle is my best friend."

Knowing Kyle was gone, Justin's choice of 'is' vs. 'was' caught Carter's attention. It was clear the friendship was at the root of shaping Justin's medical interests.

"Kyle is with me every second of every day. Me and my crew live for him." Justin rolled up his right sleeve to show a tattoo. It was a lion head, matching the high school logo with small writing underneath 'KZ 1.3.98-11.8.15'.

"I heard he was one hell of an athlete. Coach Baldwin said the best he'd ever had. I am really sorry for your loss. The closeness to that experience will certainly give you tremendous sympathy as you help others."

"Yep, I have definitely seen it impact my actions a few times already."

Anjali broke the football talk up, tapping Justin and pointing to the clock. "We will be back in a bit."

Doctor Z returned about fifteen minutes later with Justin alongside him.

"I heard you met Justin. He is a tremendous addition to our team and I hope he chooses to stay here after residency. I've known him since he was young."

Looking at the test results again, Doctor Z had the attention of Carter and Emily.

"As I told you, there isn't going to be step-by-step. Here's what I can give you."

Doctor Z handed Carter his business card with writing on the back.

- Pause, Look Around

- Understand what got you to the moment

- Don't allow one-word responses

- Don't look for step by step

"Thank you, Doctor Z. I imagine I might not see as much of you now that we are heading to the main floor."

"That may or may not be a good thing." Doctor Z smiled. "The room upstairs is ready. When you get up there, Justin will help make a few adjustments to your leg and I requested Cindy and Alexandra be the leaders on your care team. I make trips floor by floor daily, so you aren't rid of me yet."

Doctor Z looked at Emily, "Promise me you will keep Carter in check." Emily gave a thumbs up, placing the word search book into the first of two bedside bags while standing up.

As Justin reconfigured the monitors to allow for the bed to be wheeled, Doctor Z shook Carter and Emily's hands before walking out of the room.

Justin took the brake off the bed wheels. The initial movement of the bed jolted Carter to tense his back as the pain went from his right hip to his toes. Sensing the tension through Carter's clenched fists and facial expression, "Mr. Wilson, I will be as gentle as I can but I know this won't be easy."

Carter grimaced as Justin wheeled him past the center desk where Anjali waved, "I hope you have a speedy recovery."

Beyond the nurses' table, Carter saw Doctor Z with his back turned in his dedicated workspace. Hanging above his head was a photo of him, his wife, two daughters, and son, dressed in football gear for Senior Night. A wallet-sized remembrance card was lodged into the bottom of the frame.

After a few turns, Justin looked down at Carter who was biting his lip and fighting through the pain. Carter asked to reduce the pain medicine earlier in the morning but the small movements from the bed now had him frustrated with that earlier decision.

Looking to get his mind off the pain, "Justin, can I ask you something?"

"Is this a medical question? I am not approved to answer those unless a board-approved doctor is with me."

"No, no, no. Nothing work-related.... Doctor Z mentioned knowing you since you were young. How did you know him?"

The piecing together of data that drove Carter's success in the business world caused him to have a sinking feeling that he already knew what Justin's answer would be.

"Doctor Zito used to coach me and his oldest son in football."

Justin twisted his blue band around his wrist, looked at Carter, and gave a nod.

The four-minute trip from the I.C.U. to the main area of the hospital felt like an eternity. They arrived at Room 205. The curtain was drawn in the middle of the room.

"Wait, do I have a roommate?" Carter asked as Justin got the bed in place.

"It appears you do. There aren't many single rooms in the main area of the hospital. They just leave those for patients that are threats to others or need continuous monitoring."

"Maybe the beeping in the I.C.U. wasn't as bad as I thought."

Carter was able to see slightly around the room divider, gathering the first details of the man on the other side.

On the wall ahead was a plexiglass area where the patient's name and details.

Johnston, Randall 78.

Broken Hip

Prepping for Sunrise Village

Carter was familiar with Sunrise Village, a local retirement home, on his daily commute.

"As Doctor Z said, I am just your transfer agent to this part of the hospital. I am going to debrief Cindy and the team on the I.C.U. notes, surgery, and the plan Doctor Zito suggested. I will try to swing by after I move another patient."

"Sounds good and good luck, Justin."

As Justin left, Emily settled into a chair and found a new spot for the kids 'artwork and photos.

Emily came alongside Carter and whispered in his ear, "I think the quarterback that died was Doctor Z's son." She too had caught onto the suspicion Carter had.

"I don't know how I could go on with such an emotional job and be surrounded by death after something like that." Carter grabbed Emily's hand.

I miss James and Amelia. I need to prioritize them more.

"I love you, Carter." Emily kissed his forehead and felt her phone vibrating in her sweatshirt pocket. It was a FaceTime from Grandpa's phone.

The missing teeth of James were all that was in sight on the inbound FaceTime.

"I love you, buddy," Carter said as a proud father.

"Love you, Daddy. I have Grandpa's phone and was watching YouTube and then I figured out how to FaceTime you all by myself."

As the Wilsons continued on the phone, a nurse came into the room to check on the roommate. The nurse was an older woman, slightly overweight, with black curly hair, red-framed glasses, and scrubs covered with cats.

"Hey Randall, It's Cindy. I have your medicine."

"Thank you, Ms. Cindy. It looks like a beautiful day out today."

Carter just realized that his bed position gave him no view of the outside world.

"Looks like you got a new roommate." Cindy shared.

Cindy took Randall's order for dinner and put the T.V. on.

"Wheel of Fortune comes on in about 40 minutes, would you like me to put it on that channel?"

"Yes, please Ms. Cindy."

Carter laughed in his head.

When he was young, his family would sit together to watch Wheel of Fortune and Jeopardy. Grandpa still watched daily but Carter hadn't seen it in years, feeling too busy to waste his time on 'mindless' television.

Cindy emerged from behind the room divider, "You must be the Wilsons. Justin just delivered the other patient and is sitting down to get me up to speed. They already came around for the dinner orders. If I can catch them, what would you like?"

"I'll have the sub."

"I'll have a salad."

Carter and Emily must have been lucky, as the food cart arrived about ten minutes later. Emily noticed the nurse outside looking to make sure they were settled in.

"Are you hoping to come in?" Emily asked.

"I wanted to give you time with the food."

"Don't worry about it, come in," Carter yelled midbite.

The nurse in the cat scrubs entered and stood in front of Carter's bed.

"I'm Cindy, I'll be the lead on your care team. The next few days we will be getting you ready for rehabbing that leg." Cindy had been briefed on Carter and extended her introduction. "I have been at Upstate Medical for seventeen years, started first in the delivery room, and have been in this area for the past five years. So... It looks like the pins are allowing everything to set properly. You likely didn't know this but during the time in the I.C.U., the team did some massaging of the leg to ensure no blood clots formed. After you finish dinner, we will do a bit together and run through what to expect tomorrow."

"Thank you, Cindy. It's nice to meet you."

As Cindy left the room, Emily and Carter continued eating their dinner off the cafeteria trays. Emily planned to head home in a bit but enjoyed the relief of someone else making dinner.

Around 7:00 p.m., Emily grabbed her bag. "I love you. I am happy you are out of the I.C.U. Amelia has an appointment tomorrow morning so I won't get here until around lunchtime."

"I love you too. Thank you for being here through this."

After a kiss goodbye, Carter sat in the room and grabbed Doctor Z's business card off the side table.

Carter re-read the four bullet points Doctor Z scribbled on the back.

- Pause, Look Around

- Understand what got you to the moment

- Don't allow one-word responses

- Don't look for step by step

After a few minutes of silence, Randall Johnston spoke up from the other side of the curtain, "Carter Wilson, you are very fortunate."

Yellow Light 5: Appreciate the interconnectivity of others.

Six

· · · ● · ● · ● · · ·

Carter hadn't noticed Justin had written Carter's information on the plexiglass across from his bed and in sight of his new roommate.

Wilson, Carter 34

Shattered Right Leg

Begin P.T. before returning home

"Uh...yeah. Nice to meet you, Randall Johnston."

Carter always played his hand close to the chest initially and didn't love the fact someone was overhearing his business.

Cindy returned to the room to let Carter and Randall know that she was taking off, checked the monitors, and asked if they needed anything.

Carter asked for a refill of water. Randall asked if she would move the room divider slightly so he could meet Carter.

Cindy looked at Carter for approval. Carter didn't feel like there was an option to say no. So, Carter gave Cindy a slight nod, palms up, and shrug of the shoulders.

Cindy opened the curtain and left the room. Carter continued to keep his eyes shut, overhearing the category selection of the Wheel of Fortune winner for the bonus round, 'Around the House'.

Randall's bed was adjusted more upright than Carter's. With Carter's leg still elevated, he remained restricted.

After pretending to be dozing off, Carter opened his eyes.

"I'm Randall Johnston. Welcome to Room 205. I hope to be out of here and give you your own space in a few days."

Carter turned his neck slightly to put a face with the name.

Randall Johnston was an older African American man with a receding hairline, a small afro, a goatee, and a wide smile.

"Saw on your board you broke your hip and are going to Sunrise," Carter replied.

"Yeah, let's just say living alone and wet leaves can do a number on a worn body. Now that Carla is gone, they think I should be somewhere where I don't need to take care of a house and can have some activities during the day."

Looking to not get roped into a lengthy conversation, Carter replied, "I have heard Sunrise is a great place."

Emily had taken the kids to sing Christmas Carols at Sunrise last year and pictures from that were Carter's level of exposure to the facility; other than it being at the intersection of the second flashing yellow on his morning commute.

"What's someone as young and healthy looking as you doing here?" Randall asked.

"I got in a car accident a few days ago, shattered my leg, and needed emergency surgery."

"Were you the one with the mangled-up Jeep that made the morning news and caused all the traffic issues on Thursday?"

Carter had no idea. "Maybe...Let's just say there was a point they weren't sure I was going to make it. I'm just ready to get better and get out of here."

Jeopardy was just starting and Carter reminisced of his days growing up when Jeopardy was family time and Alex Trebek hosted. He was always described by Carter's father as 'A fine-dressed man.'

The Jeopardy round began, and Randall shouted out answers to the questions. "Oh, I know that play, I went with Carla. Yes...Oklahoma!"

Carter sat back enjoying watching the show and also Randall's attempts and "I knew that one" delayed responses.

"Want to join me during Double Jeopardy?" Randall asked.

"Sure."

'Cooperstown Legends' was the category that finally got Carter involved.

"Which future Hall of Famer played with his father and is the only fa-ther-son duo to hit back-to-back home runs?" Mayim Bialik asked through the TV.

"Ken Griffey Jr.," Carter shouted.

"Who is Ken Griffey Jr.?" corrected Randall. Reminding Carter, "You wouldn't have gotten points for that on the show."

Carter snickered.

The two continued until the show was over. Randall mentioned he normally looked to wind down after Jeopardy and hit the call button for the night nurse to return. She turned the T.V. off, checked the monitors, and shut off the lights.

Carter had slept most of the day so wasn't ready to call it a day.

"Hey Randall, I appreciate you letting me join you." Randall was al-ready fast asleep.

The hour of watching the gameshows was the first time at the hospital that Carter's mind wasn't racing about what was next.

Having a roommate might not be the worst thing while I am here.

Yellow Light 6: Never underestimate the joy you can find in time with a stranger.

SEVEN

· · · ● · ● · ● · ·

CARTER WOKE UP AND looked at the clock on the wall, 7:36 a.m.

Normally he would have been in the office and through the backlog of emails. It was Monday and it had been years since Carter slept in that late on a weekday and even rarely that late on weekends, other than after travel weeks to Asia.

Randall had the morning news on already. Today the team was going to remove the pins stabilizing holding Carter's elevated leg and transition to a brace.

"Morning, Carter" Randall called from behind the curtain, after hearing Carter's stretching groans.

"Hey, Randall."

Cindy stood in the doorway. "Another blessed day; I will come to take the breakfast orders soon."

Randall already had the T.V. going, the newscasters were talking about the various fall festivals over the next few weeks and the Top-Rated D.I.Y. Halloween costumes for the year.

"Cindy is awesome." Randall shared.

"She seems nice."

"Carter, tell me more about yourself."

Jesus, man! I just woke up, give me some time to breathe.

Carter started the day questioning his decision to engage in watching Jeopardy last night.

"I just woke up. Can I have a few minutes?"

Randall didn't reply and continued watching the news.

Carter noticed Randall looking out the window from his bed and began to hear humming. It took some time before Carter picked up the tune...Come Together by The Beatles.

"Sorry, Randall. Normally I am out of the house and the morning is pretty quiet."

Carter did consider himself a morning person, an early riser, who accomplished more by 10:00 a.m. than what he felt others did their entire day. Most of his morning was spent in isolation, minus the radio on the commute and email addresses on the other side of his continuously filling inbox

"I grew up here, went away for school, joined a start-up, got my M.B.A. at night, and lead product strategy at a big tech company."

"Gotcha. Some cool accomplishments. Is what you've done who you are?"

So much for me being friendly. We got an interrogator here.

"Mr. Randall Johnston, why don't you tell me more about yourself?"

Sensing the tension Randall delayed his response.

"I am a father of two boys, widower to my wife who passed from cancer, Vietnam Veteran, former town employee, and a volunteer at my church."

Seeing the difference in the response Randall provided to his own, Carter sat quietly digesting the weather forecast on the TV.

As the commercial break happened, Randall asked "So did you meet Doctor Z?"

"Yeah," Carter replied.

"He seems liked by everyone here. Seems to have created a unique culture amongst the staff."

Carter thought about how the culture at his company, M.E.Z., had changed in recent years. When he joined, he and his colleague collaborated much more. The work was more fun and energizing to Carter back then when he was focused on helping the new employees to learn all about the products and their important role in the day-to-day success. Some of the culture change he equated to everyone getting older and some to more outside investments into the company putting increased pressure on performance and reporting.

"Yeah, Doctor Z seems like a bright guy. When I was wheeled over here I discovered about his oldest son Kyle being the quarterback who passed away about a decade back."

Randall set down the water cup he had been holding in his hand. He brought his hands together on the bridge of his nose and shook his head back and forth

Randall finally looked up and towards Carter, "My kids are my everything. I can't imagine."

"I don't think I could stay in this sort of profession if it was me," Carter replied, thinking about James and Amelia.

"Randall, you mentioned having three kids last night, right?"

"No, just two boys. They are fifteen years apart. Let's just say that in your mid-fifties having a second child is a big surprise. Carla was younger but still a big surprise for her too.

My older son, Christian, moved away after meeting a girl in college and his son, Cameron, is going to turn eight." Randall's smile glowed as he continued, "R.J. is wrapping up undergrad in December. Not to my liking but he decided to add a second major in organizational psychology his junior year, so it meant another semester."

There was a knock on the already open door to Room 205. Cindy arrived alongside Doctor Z. Doctor Z entered the room briskly as if the visits on the main floor followed a different rhythm than those in the I.C.U.

"Carter, Randall, big few days coming up for you both. Let's chat a bit. Do you mind if we do one W.P.G. session as a room?"

Doctor Z cleared the whiteboard in front of Carter's bed and wrote in all caps, 'SYSTEM'.

"I want today to involve reflection on your support system." Carter and Randall watched Doctor Z.

"Randall, you go first for the one-word priority." Doctor

"Movement."

Doctor Z wrote the word and turned pointing to Carter.

"Healing"

"Cindy, your turn."

"Prioritize."

Without turning, Doctor Z continued writing. "I am going to write the goal I hope each of you achieves."

Next to each priority provided by Carter, Randall, and Cindy, Doctor Z completed the chart.

Doctor Z stepped away. "Some days are better than others and sometimes your own goals must be put aside to address another's goals for you."

"I am sorry I am in a rush. We had a teenage suicide from an overdose last night and those I.C.U. updates are always tough to stomach. Good luck today and I will be back again tomorrow."

Cindy, Randall, and Carter all remained frozen, reading the whiteboard in their heads.

Cindy was the first to move, taking the breakfast trays from Carter and Randall. "Carter, we will start removing the stabilizers in about an hour. Randall, the care manager for Sunrise normally comes early in the afternoon."

As Cindy left the room, Carter turned towards Randall.

"Well, that definitely didn't seem like the same Doctor Z we know."

"Yeah. I mean, still, to this day certain sounds get me shaken up from my time in Vietnam."

"I feel like Doctor Z put system because today is a day where he needs his own."

"Yeah, that could very well be the case," Randall said, now looking out at the fall foliage.

Cindy returned alongside another nurse who introduced herself. Cindy's eyes looked swollen and her cheeks red from crying.

"Good morning, my name is Alexandra."

Alexandra was short with blonde hair and freckles and looked as if she could have passed for a student at a college campus.

"Cindy is going to be taking off, so I'll be stepping in. I am going to help get your leg a bit more comfortable, Mr. Wilson."

With little get-to-know-you time, Alexandra jumped right in.

As Cindy simply waved goodbye without a word, Randall took notice of Doctor Z's goal for Cindy on the whiteboard.

Trying to build some confidence, and rapport, while knowing other patients often treated her as just a kid, Alexandra discussed her experience.

"I just helped last week with a similar injury. I am going to put some pillows alongside and below."

Alexandra went to the standing closet in the room and grabbed two extra pillows off the top shelf.

"This isn't going to be comfortable but I will bring you medicine right after to dull the pain."

Already sensing some pain from the pillow slightly leaning against his leg, Carter bit his lip and clenched the side railing as Alexandra lowered his leg further and removed the stabilization brackets. Carter's gown had slid up and his leg was visible. The gown was now in the middle of his thigh. Carter's leg was completely shaved, now with just a little stubble around the discolored and indistinguishable knee joint where the stitches began.

After the adjustments by Alexandra, a soft brace was put on, leaving Carter's leg looking like a hotdog.

Alexandra went to the monitor and location where the liquid I.V., catheter, and medical bags hung. She adjusted the medicine bag to increase the flow of the pain medicine.

The pain caused a wave of exhaustion and the remainder of the morning Carter spent napping.

Around 11:00 a.m., he woke to Emily's voice. Randall had caught her ear.

"Yeah, he lost the first one a few months back and the other got bumped out on the playground at school. That was fun to explain how the Tooth

Fairy had found it in the school grass and still wanted to give him a few dollars under his pillow."

Carter squinted before opening his eyes completely. He saw Randall holding a school photo of James.

"Good morning, babe," Carter said, breaking up the discussion on James' photo.

Emily approached Carter's bed and kissed him.

"I see you have your own human jack-o-lantern." Randall joked with James' photo still in hand.

Emily smiled back at Randall.

Now rubbing Carter's hair from his forehead, "I see they adjusted your leg. How are you feeling?"

"One step closer to being out of here."

Alexandra walked by the door and Emily held up some fun-size packs of candy.

"Are they able to have any of these?" nodding her head in Randall and Carter's direction.

"It won't hurt them but don't give him too much," Alexandra replied, pointing to the further bed where Randall was laying.

As Emily handed Carter the Sour Patch, he yelled over to Randall. "You want a thing of candy?"

"Oh, yeah! Just remember, candy makes the Snickers come out of an old man."

"Wow..." Carter chuckled and threw a bag of fun-sized Starburst onto Randall's lap. Emily walked a thing of Skittles over.

Randall smiled, "Skittles, my favorite. For years I'd pick these up in the morning with my coffee. How did you think I maintained such a good physique?"

The room broke out in laughter.

Emily's laughter stopped as she looked down at her phone. It was her boss calling. She had coordinated coverage this week but wasn't sure how long everything was going to be like it was. Carter caught parts of half of the conversation Emily had while standing outside the doorway.

"Yeah, we should find out more today."

"Tell Jamie he can call me if he has any questions on how to handle it."

"I appreciate you letting me take time even though I am still in the orientation period."

"Thank you! I will."

"Bye"

Emily returned to the room, deep breaths evident as her shoulder went up and down.

Sensing anxiety, Carter asked, "How did that go?"

Emily couldn't get out words, she just buried her head into Carter's shoulder and started to cry. Thoughts flooded her brain.

Why did this have to happen when it did? I just started this new job, and love it, and we are backtracking on my revised independence.

Embracing his wife, "I love you. I am sorry this happened."

"This is just a lot all at once."

Emily finally stood up and noticed a short man with a teal long-sleeve polo speaking with Alexandra at the door. The shirt had the Sunrise Senior Living logo.

The man stepped in and privately began reviewing paperwork and logistics for Randall's transition to assisted living.

"Mr. Johnston, you live on your own now, correct?"

"Yes. My youngest son is due to graduate in December but I don't think he's going to be staying around here. I don't want to put a burden on him."

"How has the physical therapy been going?"

"I just started last week but it's coming along and I know I'll need a walker for a while."

"How are you feeling about coming to Sunrise?"

"I don't really know."

Still feeling the emotions of the call from her boss, Emily, and Carter weren't talking as the man spoke to Randall just a few feet away. Carter was eavesdropping more than Emily but both heard that last question and response.

"Okay, well I will stay in touch with the hospital on your exit plan and am happy to support you in any way."

Emily looked at Carter. "He's not going to Sunrise."

Yellow Light 7: Share goals with and for others and accept progress and movement are different things.

EIGHT

· · · · ● · ● · · · ·

EMILY THOUGHT ABOUT HER parents. Her mother spent the last two years in a nursing home after her father passed from a heart attack.

At the time, Emily and Carter lived far away. Emily was always sacrificing for Carter and once she became pregnant with James, the four-hour flights to visit her family were a challenge. In fact, Emily canceled a trip the weekend before her mother passed. This was often a topic brought up during arguments between her and Carter.

Emily knew the struggle Randall felt, her mother felt it too. Like Emily's mother, Randall appeared to be addressing the huge decision with limited support around.

Emily needed to be back home by 4:00 p.m. that first day Carter was on the main floor. The physical therapy team planned to drop by to discuss the rehab strategy and she wanted to hear the plans firsthand.

Throughout the afternoon, except for a few visits by Alexandra checking in, Randall remained quiet with the room divider partially pulled. The theme music of Law and Order every thirty minutes must have meant a marathon on T.N.T.

At around 3:00 p.m. Alexandra stopped by to let Carter and Emily know that the physical therapy team wouldn't arrive until 4:30 p.m.

"Are you kidding me?" Emily grunted as she clenched her fist.

Emily decided to head out right then to relieve her in-laws for a few hours.

After Emily took off, Randall shouted, "Cherish your family. Now that I am older, I have more days behind me than ahead."

Randall's vibrancy and positivity from the day before seemed a bit dampened by the thought of Sunrise being the spot where he could spend the remainder of his days.

"I'm sorry, Randall. What would make you feel better?" Carter asked.

Randall let out a deep breath. "I don't know. I just envy the life you still have to live. I am being shipped off and put in a cage with a bunch of old people dying every day."

Carter sat thinking. *How can I relate to this guy? He's more than double my age.*

He seemed in such a good mood yesterday. First Doctor Z, now Randall. I'm never normally the one in the best mood of everyone.

"Randall, let's get your mind off what will happen after the hospital for a bit. Tell me more about what you were doing when you were my age."

The curtain still closed between the two, Randall reached out to hit the back of the divider a bit. He was now able to see just Carter's face.

"I started on a garbage truck for the town after returning from Vietnam. I remember starting first on the back of the car because I didn't have my driver's license. I spent my first few paychecks on driving classes so I could move inside the truck as the winter approached.

Carla was pregnant with Christian at that time and to put it bluntly, I wasn't myself in the early days coming back from 'Nam'.

"You would have to pay me double what I make now to deal with that job."

"Well...it worked for me and to this day I am getting paid a pension for the thirty years I put in. Nowadays, it's tough to get anyone to do work with their hands."

Carter never had a manual labor job other than cutting the neighbor's grass in high school and knew very little of what the day-to-day looked like for a sanitation worker.

Randall's mind was definitely off Sunrise. Carter hit a topic that Randall would have lots to talk about.

"Have you ever had to drive a truck that big?"

"I drove a fifteen-foot U-Haul when Emily and I moved between apartments. It was only a twenty-minute drive but I still remember how stressful it was."

"Yeah. The truck I drove was twenty-four feet. It was a monster. Very few people realize it but just like the U-Hauls you can rent, you have to rely on the side view mirrors only. Got in a few crashes myself in the thirty years. Once because of snow and two other times because of the idiots always in a rush passing on double yellows."

Carter listened in and nodded, guilty of being 'that guy'.

"During the training that they put me through, the one piece of information that stuck in my brain was 'you can't look back and that there was a reason even in standard cars that the windshield is larger than the rearview mirror. Rely on looking to your left and right for support."

Carter could see Randall's mood improving as he told the story of his favorite route and the truth of how much the garbage workers made in tips for the holiday, including how the gift cards left on the cans normally covered his morning coffee trips through April.

"The best part was I would take the cash tips and Carla would plan a vacation to a new state we'd never been to each year. I loved the memories we made on those trips."

Carter listened patiently as the story continued, filling time and bringing Randall back to a happier place.

Randall wrapped the long monologue with a comment that showed that he found a bit of clarity. "Your eyes must be looking forward. Wishing you took a different turn or that the conditions around you were different just drains energy. I have to accept this moment and accept that what is next is unknown."

Carter realized he and Randall had way more in common than he thought. "I need to accept the moment too and stay going forward even if I don't know what's ahead."

Randall looked out the window and appeared to wipe a tear from his face.

"Thank you for letting me talk. Carla used to be so good at listening that I often would solve my own dilemmas just through a listening ear and my own thoughts."

At that moment a young man entered the room.

"Hey, Randall. I am here to see your new roommate. Tomorrow morning you have your physical therapy. You did a great job standing with the walker yesterday."

The physical therapist turned to Carter. "Hi Carter, my name is John."

John had a similar build to Carter, about six-foot with broad shoulders. John had a short beard and a skin-tight fade, with slick-backed hair on the top. He wore fresh white sneakers.

"We'll do the first session here in the room and I'll do most of the work."

John first started by removing Carter's socks.

"Fair warning, my feet are pretty gross." Emily always said Carter had caveman feet due to all the blisters and broken toenails Carter had from running.

"I appreciate the warning. Seeing the wear and tear of another active person is better than what I see with the bunions and varicose veins of most of the people I deal with."

Looking to gauge nerve reactions, John scratched the bottom of Carter's foot and started rotating Carter's ankle slowly.

The leg injury, despite severe, was more from the knee joint and tibia. That said, then ankle movement still triggered muscle and nerves to pulse around the more impacted area. Carter grimaced as he was asked to attempt to pull his toes up and then down. Despite John's hands being on Carter's feet, zero resistance was being applied.

John unstrapped the brace to check the healing of the wound and where the stitches were. He wanted to make sure there wasn't anything hidden under the brace.

John looked at the bruising and swelling. "I always found it pretty wild when I started in this field how some older people would walk out of the hospital even the same day as a complete knee replacement. The lower leg stuff and reconstruction takes time."

"Do you think I will be able to walk out of the hospital when I leave?" Carter asked.

"Definitely not. You had more than a knee replacement, the rod where your tibia was is a big deal and it will be about 6 months before you can think about the possibility of getting any more blisters on your feet." John said half joking.

John adjusted the soft brace that went from Carter's calf to the middle of his thigh. The simple adjustment agitated Carter who let out a "FUCK..."

"I'm sorry man. I am going to put some stim on it for a few minutes before we do anything else." John applied three sticky pads, one on each side of Carter's calf, the other on his quad."

Carter gripped the bedside railing until his fingers were white. He then looked down to see that the stim setting was only on two.

John took a warm heating pad off the cart he had wheeled in and set a timer for ten minutes.

"I am going to stay right here and after the timer beeps we will look to put a low wedge under your knee to see how the joint reacts to it being bent."

Carter shut his eyes, remembering that just three weeks prior he completed a 10k race fundraising for Leukemia and Lymphoma and finished fourth in the thirty to thirty-five age division.

How am I going to do this for six months? How do they expect me to do this when I go back to work? What will happen when Emily is on the road traveling for her job?

The ten minutes felt like forever. "Is this almost done?"

"Not yet," John said, now standing in front of Randall and taking in the colors of the leaves on the hillside in the distance.

After the stim session, John removed the stim and heating pad. He had a small triangle-shaped wedge about five inches from the base to point in his hands.

"I am going to slide this up from your toe to behind your knee." John worked diligently and with gentleness.

Most of his patients were older and more sensitive. The wedge slid slowly up the back of Carter's calf. Carter bit down and grasped the bedside railing again.

"Your leg hasn't bent this much for a few days so it's going to hurt. The muscles and tendons were extremely strained, and some were torn."

"Fuck, fuck, fuck!"

"This is the last thing we will do today. Tomorrow, we will try to sit you up."

Carter had seen Randall get a newspaper delivered earlier and heard a pen hit the floor. "John, can you grab that, I'm almost done with the crossword."

John grabbed the pen and walked it over to Randall. Randall whispered. "You will have to break through Carter's façade of strength."

Similar to the ten-minute wait with the stimulation, Carter sat with the wedge under his leg as John looked on.

"So, is this what you expected for today?" Carter asked a bit frustrated with the limited progress he felt was made.

"It's in line with what I thought would happen."

After John was gone, Carter looked over to Randall. "This fucking sucks."

"What do you mean?"

"I can't even get out of bed. I don't know when I will walk. I'm missing the final quarter of the year, and it's Halloween in a few days."

Randall stared blankly at Carter, "When are you going to remove your mask of armor?"

The room fell silent.

Yellow Light 8: Keep your eyes forward and know that sometimes pedal to the floor is not an option.

NINE

· · · · ● · ● · · · ·

CARTER WISHED HE COULD move and jump across the room. His blood pressure was through the roof. Comments like that at work caused him to have a reputation for being hot-headed, which leadership defused by saying on multiple locations... 'Carter is just passionate and needs to tone it back sometimes.' It was the same hot temper that left a scar through his left eyebrow from a bar fight in college.

"EXCUSE ME?!?! What the fuck does that mean?" Carter exploded at Randall.

Although Randall knew Carter was immobile, he found himself sinking back into the bed with fear of seeing a person half of his age act so aggressively.

"We all put up facades. I think you've hidden behind accomplishments and don't really know who you are or what you want." Randall replied.

Fucking old man.

"You don't even know me you dick, and how dare you. Now I am learning why your family wants to put you in a home versus dealing with your shit."

"Son, I have forty-plus years on you and I can tell you a whole hell of a lot about life if you actually cared to let anyone else into shaping Carter's golden vision of his future."

The loud spat caught the attention of Alexandra who was about to head into Room 203 next door.

"Are you guys doing all right in there?" Alexandra asked as she peered in, knowing to expect some sort of a smart response.

"Yes, Ms. Alexandra, just helping Carter realize the strength in vulnerability," Randall replied.

Alexandra saw Carter close his eyes and release deep breaths. She was able to see his lips moving and counting to ten.

Carter was out of the driver's seat and it was right where he needed to be.

"Randall, I am going to choose to stop this conversation."

"Well, I'm not looking to talk to the voice responding to me; I'm looking to talk with your heart and the Carter that's two layers deeper. Let me know when that person gets their head out of their ass." Randall said, getting in the last word.

Carter ignored the comment and closed his eyes. Randall could see Carter directly. After a few minutes and in a noticeable state of being more relaxed, Randall spoke.

"The answer of who you are has deep roots. We each have our own journey of accomplishments and pitfalls. I'm not perfect. I had to join the army because I lost a college scholarship. Why I got behind the wheel that night after being out still bothers me to this day. Thankfully no one got hurt when I crashed the car. That's the same reason I had to get my license again before I started driving the garbage truck. It seems like you may have been more successful than others or at least at elevating those accomplishments in front of the fails or pitfalls but I know the same type of low points I mentioned exist somewhere. Stop speeding through life looking for the next trophy to lift."

Despite Carter closing his eyes tighter, he was hearing every word. Randall looked outside as the streetlights started to click on.

Randall continued, "A barricade of strength falls hardest when it is facing pressures it hasn't had in years. You may feel like that is what happened to you last week. The façade you've built, is that truly who Carter is and who Carter wants to be?"

Carter was no longer frustrated. Carter realized the argument was spawned out of a genuine desire to prompt improvement.

"Sit with the question Carter, because I know you are listening. You just blew up at me. If you aren't willing to change, that's the type of person your family will remember you as. Not the guy who provides everything for them, but the guy who can't deal with not being 100% in control. When you leave here, who do you want to be and how can this experience change you and your future for the better?"

The next two hours in the room were chillingly silent. The T.V. was off and Randall continued reading the paper.

Randall's standard 7:00 p.m. television hour of Wheel of Fortune and Jeopardy was only a few minutes away.

"You know what Randall? I haven't had someone leave me speechless like that in a very long time."

Randall turned and made eye contact. "I was scared when you blew up at me. I know I'm not the only person to see you in that form. I may just be an old man who you spend a few days with at the hospital. I get that you have been successful and that's great. What frustrates me the most is that there are pieces to Carter as a person that aren't being embraced. You and your family's future can be even better than the path you have been on if you just accept you aren't able to control some things."

Pat Sajak came on the screen and Vanna White walked to the wheel as Carter gave a slight nod of his head.

Randall turned his attention to the T.V. and said, "Let's take a break from the conversation for now but I want you to appreciate that only through vulnerability will your authenticity be found."

Carter felt like he had his own Yoda in this seventy-something, retired garbage truck driver.

There was no interaction aside from answers blurted out during Wheel. Emily called Carter during the first round of Jeopardy. Carter knew the window from 7:30 p.m. to 8:00 p.m. in the Wilson house was usually the most hectic and he could sense exhaustion in his wife's voice.

"Hey babe. How are the kids?"

"Oh, yeah?"

"When do you have to do that?"

"Okay, so tomorrow you will come after school with the kids. Got it."

"James just did what?"

"Yeah, go handle it. I love you. I don't show or say it enough but the sacrifices you make for our family are appreciated."

Emily hung up first. James had opened the front door and Zeus was running around the neighborhood. Thankfully the neighbors all had dogs and Zeus normally just ran to be face to face with the first dog he saw.

Alexandra stopped by to check in on Randall and Carter before taking off for the night. "Have a good night, guys. Remember John will be back early for therapy for both of you."

"Goodnight." The men said in unison.

"Randall?"

Randall was slow to reply. This was normally his wind-down time. "My rest can wait because yours has yet to begin."

"What do you mean I wear a mask?"

"I just can tell that there are pieces of you that are protected in fear of some sort of pain or fear of showing weakness. How do you think you are viewed at work? Do you feel as connected as you wish you were to your wife? Do you spend the time you should with your family?"

Carter asked for the conversation so despite the urge to snap in anger like earlier in the day he simply said, "Go on."

"You are probably in one of the most vulnerable positions you have been physically in years. Mentally you haven't had this amount of time to just sit with your feelings for years. The simple fact you are listening shows you are emotionally broken from all of this. It's great you feel you can power through this pain but it's not sustainable to push yourself the way you are."

Randall paused a bit and grabbed the final sip of his orange juice left over from dinner.

"When you open yourself up, you become more approachable. Your relationships grow because you recognize how much you need others. Your value increases because vulnerability exposes authenticity. Your authentic self and the strengths you don't know you have, those have been subdued." Randall looked across to see if Carter had anything to say. Carter's eyes were squeezed in thought.

"I am getting tired. I will leave you to think more about it." Randall hit the button near the bed to dim the lights.

Yellow Light 9: A key to authenticity is vulnerability.

TEN

· · · ● · ● · ● · ● · ·

CARTER STAYED UP DIGESTING the entire day. The last glimpse of the clock said 11:42 p.m. Working through his feelings and thoughts brought a wave of emotions to Carter. Negative and positive memories left Carter's head spinning. A majority of the thoughts were around Emily and the kids. Carter however still struggled to not tie every bad action back to something he was impacted by at work. Being a parent and carrying a heavy stress load at work is not easy for anyone. It is especially difficult for Type A people like Carter.

The barrier is there! It's my way to separate the different areas of my life. What if I just let everything blend together?

Carter reminisced about countless situations where his approachability limited the progression toward solving an issue and weakened his relationship with others.

Just last week, there were blowouts at work and home.

At work, the engineering team at M.E.Z. only saw the closed-door of Carter while he was at the office. They cringed as Carter walked by. Stalin was his nickname by some of the younger engineers.

The engineering team missed a huge client upgrade that was promised to be delivered. Instead of feeling like they could approach Carter with the news on Wednesday, they delayed telling him until a weekly call on Friday.

Similarly, Carter returned home last Tuesday and walked through the garage to find an empty box with a picture of a toilet on the side. It wasn't until he checked the banking app on his phone that he saw a pending charge for Jake's Plumbing. Rather than let Carter know about the 'swimming adventure' of Amelia's toys while she was being 'watched' by Gram, Emily just got a plumber out to the house and had it handled.

My wife doesn't even feel comfortable telling me things for fear of me exploding. When other people at work have tried to tell me about their issues at home impacting their work, why have I not turned around and looked to be a support? Did anyone with a brain think the perfect life I painted and portrayed was a reality?

What good does putting up the barrier bring? Let's try tomorrow to peel the layers of the mask.

The next morning, Carter woke up to Cindy's voice.

"My mother has dementia and had a big setback earlier in the week. I am sorry I had to leave."

Randall had been up for some time. "Never apologize for having your priorities in order."

"Alexandra mentioned that Carter started physical therapy with John and that his kids might be dropping by today?"

The audible yawn gave Cindy and Randall a warning that the masked man was waking up.

"Good morning, Mr. Wilson."

"Hi, Cindy. Welcome back."

"I might have missed it but did you say your mother had something happen earlier in the week?"

Showing this level of interest felt strange as Carter asked the question.

"Oh, yes. She's okay now. It's just difficult when you see people's minds go and be so oblivious to common things."

It was not meant to be an underhanded comment towards Carter at all but after the time alone last night, Carter did feel in the same boat as Cindy's mother, oblivious to common things.

Cindy continued to share some more details about her mother's dementia.

Doctor Z then arrived.

"Morning, gentlemen."

Randall gave a wave and Carter threw up the peace sign.

"Carter, how did day one of therapy go?"

"Pretty painful to be honest. John also mentioned six months of therapy which wasn't what I hoped to hear."

Randall let out a laugh. "I thought Carter was going to bite his lip off and he has some ugly-looking feet."

Doctor Z already got the low down from John but wanted to get Carter's view.

"John must have done the first session in the room then?"

"Yeah. Some stretching, stim pads, some massage, and this wedge thing to bend my knee a little."

"Got it. That's good you did that much. I have a busy day today but wanted to make sure I dropped by to check in. I also heard your kids will be swinging by so I brought them these little fidget spinners."

He dropped the spinners on the bedside table and walked towards the whiteboard and wrote the word, 'COUNSEL'.

"You know the drill; priorities and goals now. I will write mine and then you each will share."

Doctor Z wrote 'selflessness' as his priority and 'see the right things' as his goal.

"Okay, Mr. Johnston...Whatcha got?" looking over his shoulder at Randall.

"'Decisiveness' for my priority and 'clarify advice' for my goal." Doctor Z appeared to wink at Randall as he turned to Carter.

"'Vulnerable' and 'become more approachable'". Carter added.

"Wow, gents! We got some deep stuff on this board.

Carter, how has everything been with the transition to the main floor? I heard you boys had some war of words yesterday?"

It seemed like Doctor Z had insight into everything going on at the hospital.

Carter looked over at Randall. "Randall is a wise man and he's just trying to heal more than just physically during my time here."

Doctor Z smiled. "I knew it was worth suggesting putting you guys together. Have a great day."

Doctor Z shuffled out of the room as the breakfast cart entered and Carter and Randall dove into the pancakes.

After a few bites, "I wonder how Doctor Z decides what to put on each board."

Randall sipped his orange juice and replied. "I think he uses a few over and over. Last week I had 'COUNSEL' as the main word and my old roommate taught me something about it. It was why I had Doctor Z write 'clarify advice' for my goal."

Carter saw the weather forecast on the T.V. screen. The anticipated storms for later in the week on Halloween appeared to be less likely. He was happy knowing it wouldn't ruin the plans Emily had for the kids.

"So do you think advice and counsel are the same thing?" Randall asked.

"Umm, I guess so. I imagine in the dictionary they are."

"So... the person in here before you made it clear they aren't. George was almost ninety and also broke his hip. Very, very nice man, although he hated my interactive take on Wheel and Jeopardy to the point where he asked the nurse to bring in headphones."

Carter laughed. If it weren't for the baseball questions in Double Jeopardy and growing up with the memories of Alex Trebec, he might have made the same request.

Randall continued, "Doctor Z knows the importance of us all finding a support system. That's his premise around always making sure each patient has 'COUNSEL' added as a word in the W.P.G. whiteboard sessions.

When he wrote it last week, George, a former attorney, dove deep into the word. George, Doctor Z, and I had a long chat on what counsel meant and it sparked a great discovery that I'd like to teach you."

Carter picked up his coffee and got more comfortable in the bed.

The monologues he'd heard from Randall in the past had far less of a set-up so he figured this one must be good.

"Thinking advice and counsel are the same is common but there are vast differences between the two. We often ask others, can I have some advice? We ask that when a majority of the time counsel is really what is desired and needed."

Carter had turned his head fully to Randall, continuing to sip the coffee. Randall went on.

"You ready for the main point?"

"You got my attention, Randall."

"Advice is delivered with I in mind. Counsel is all about you."

"I'm tracking what you are saying."

"Advice results in the other person attempting to put themselves in your shoes. I hated when people did that."

"Me too! There is too much at the core of each person and situation to trust advice as a path to follow."

Randall nodded, sharing a similar feeling to Carter, and continued.

"Advice language will sound like, 'If I were you,' 'When I was' or 'I suggest'. Counsel language instead sounds like this: 'What is driving YOU to feel that way?', 'How would that impact other things important to YOU?', 'Assume the decision is made one way or the other, how does it feel for you to live with that being the decision?' Counsel results in the discovery and creation of your own path. This is how a human's greatest clarity and confidence in decisions occur."

Carter sat with the words of his personal Yoda.

"Does that make sense to you?" Randall asked, finishing off his orange juice.

"It does."

Carter had moved his hand to his chin, digesting it more.

Would being more mindful of this change how ideas and opinions were heard and acted on?

Cindy knocked on the open door and mentioned that she had Randall's son R.J. on the line.

Despite a few days in the room, this was the first time Randall got a call.

"Can I send the call to your phone?"

"Of course!"

Cindy patched the call from the main desk into Randall's bedside phone.

Carter caught some pieces of Randall's side of the call.

"Yeah, that sounds good. I'd love to see you. Aunt Kim can drive you back next Thursday if you want to just get a one-way bus pass."

"That's great news! I am proud of you son."

"Love you too"

After Randall hung up the phone, he looked toward Carter with an expanded brightness on his face.

"R.J. is going to come home for fall break next week."

"That's awesome. I hope I can meet him"

"I hope so too. He's stayed at school for the past two years since his mother passed. It was around this time of year so it's been tough for him to come back home and probably won't be easy for him to see me in the hospital."

Carter thought about how quickly James and Amelia were growing up and the moments he missed so far.

Every parent wants their children to grow up, be happy, and do something they love, contributing to the greater good.

"R.J. was easier to raise than Christian. He's a good kid and really cares about others...Children are the greatest joy."

Carter stared blankly, zoning out about advice vs. counsel.

"Did you always want kids? Hello? Carter, did you always want kids?"

"Sorry Randall, I zoned out. What did you say?"

"Kids. Did you want them?"

"I saw myself having kids. Emily was more committed to it happening when it did than me. I didn't change a diaper before James came around. I was pretty useless until the kids got to around two.

Randall could tell Carter had a strong love for his family but courageously asked, "Do you think your current lifestyle matches your values and view of what you want your family to remember you as?"

That was a bit of a dagger question there.

"Things could improve," Carter answered timidly and sat with his thoughts.

I think my heart and mind have as much strengthening to do as my leg.

Randall smiled wittingly, "I just asked you questions with YOU in mind. How much deeper did you have to dig for answers because of that?"

This was Randall helping to demonstrate the key difference between advice and counsel.

Yellow Light 10: Understand the difference between advice and counsel.

ELEVEN

· · · ● · ● · · ·

CARTER AND RANDALL BOTH had physical therapy later that morning. Randall completed some cycles around the room with the walker and Carter got to sit in the wheelchair, scooting with some assistance from John.

"Carter, before you can leave, we will need to get your leg stronger and you will have to get comfortable with crutches," John shared while amping up the stim machine.

The tendons around Carter's swollen leg start to pulse a bit.

John brushed the scuff off the top of his Jordans and stood alongside Carter.

"During all of these sessions, I want you to stay focused more on your mindset than the movements we make. Changes in mindset trigger progress faster than changes in actual movement. Many people start physical therapy thinking that movement means progress. Pushing too hard too fast can take the progress we make back multiple steps. It's fun to deal with people like you that want to learn the exercises and go."

John began massaging Carter's leg. "We will do some stretches today after the stim. When the body and mind are stretched, that's when discovery and progress occur. I am going to ask that you take care of yourself. You must take care of yourself to be able to take care of others."

Carter sat with his upper body propped against the wall and legs extended on the table.

"John, how'd you know you wanted to get into physical therapy?"

"The way half of the people I know do. We get injured, push too hard to get back to what we were doing, and wind up needing physical therapy ourselves."

"How'd you get injured?"

"Shoulder. Baseball. College."

As the two continued chatting and John took the stim patches off, Carter joked, "So I saw Alexandra, the nurse, has eyes for you."

"Haha! You think? She seems a little out of my league." The thought now planted in John's mind.

"Yeah, man. I have a good read on those things."

Rather than jump into expert advice mode, Carter thought about the advice vs. counsel conversation.

Let me test this whole thing out.

"Why do you feel that way about her being out of your league?" followed by "What's causing you to have fear in asking her on a date?" then, "How do you envision that sort of interaction taking place?"

Carter relaxed.

Carter was less interested in his takeaways from the conversation and more focused on putting John in a place where John could dig into his own feelings. John did a few assisted stretches with Carter and put some ice on Carter's leg before turning his attention to Randall. As John was walking away, Carter shouted loud enough for most nearby to hear.

"You told me that mindset matters, John. I hope that through the counsel in those questions, your mindset may have changed. No need to fear, the worst thing she could do is say no."

John blushed a little, as the other patients looked his way. "Using my own words against me. Smooth one Mr. Wilson."

Carter left the session with John and felt extremely sore physically but mentally invigorated. Carter was excited knowing that Emily, James, and Amelia would be arriving soon.

Randall and Carter were back in Room 205 less than ten minutes before they heard the sound of children in the hallway.

They heard Cindy and the other nurses.

"Hi Mario, Hi Yoshi, Hi Princess Peach."

Emily waved and hushed the children hopping and pretending to go down warp pipes.

"Sorry for all the noise, Cindy. They snuck a few pieces of candy on the way in."

"I understand. Carter and Randall just got back from physical therapy."

James peered into Room 203.

"Not that one!" Emily grabbed the back of James' Mario costume as she pointed to the door of 205.

"Daddy!" James ran to Carter, squeezing his neck and bumping slightly into the bed.

"Ow, ow, ow. Buddy."

The jostle of the bed caused some shooting pains down Carter's leg. Carter now squeezed James back.

While hugging Carter, James noticed Randall over his daddy's shoulder.

Randall gave a wink and a little wave. James let go of Carter and retreated towards the door where Amelia arrived dressed as Princess Peach, next to an adult-size Yoshi.

"Amelia, there's an old man with daddy."

Amelia, normally the social butterfly stayed right next to Emily's leg.

"Hello, sweetheart. I like your Princess Peach costume!" Carter said smiling.

Emily saw Randall looking over and Amelia squeezing tightly to her leg.

"James and Amelia, Daddy's roommate over there is named Randall. He had an accident too and is healing up."

James waved and said, "Were you in the truck that hit my daddy?"

Randall laughed, as he saw James already had some of Carter's inquisitiveness.

"James, I live alone and am really old. I fell on some wet leaves outside and broke my hip."

James stepped between the two hospital beds looking up at the brace around Randall's waist.

Amelia had finally let go of Emily's leg and went into the song. "The hip bone is connected to the leg bone. The leg bone is connected to the foot bone."

"AMELIA! Please sit down. JAMES! You too."

Mario and Princess Peach followed their mother Yoshi's command and headed to the chair in front of the beds.

"Thank you," Emily said exhaustedly to the kids, then turned to Randall and Carter.

"We brought you each a little goodie bag."

"James, please give this one to Randall."

"Amelia, give this one to Daddy."

"Mr. Randall, here you go.

"Thank you, James. Your daddy has told me a lot about you and said he's very proud of you."

James did his excited little bounce and turned back to dance alongside his little sister.

To avoid making too much noise on the floor, Emily shut the door.

"The kids have another trunk or treat tonight so we will only stay for about forty minutes. Amelia did bring a book that she wanted you to read though."

Emily pulled off her backpack and pulled out a dark green hardcover book. It was one Carter recognized immediately.

"Amelia started reading with your mom this week." Emily shared.

'The Adventures of Winnie the Pooh', the spine of the book read.

Carter remembered being about James' age when he learned to read. His father started Carter reading one line, then one paragraph, then one page, and by the end of the book, he was able to read a full two pages of the chapter book.

Carter remembered finishing the book around Christmas time and getting a Tigger stuffed animal from his grandma.

"Okay, let's read it."

Carter began reading about Pooh. "....and there was a boy named Christopher Robin."

"Let me see, let me see." Amelia pulled at the bottom of the book.

Emily grabbed Amelia at the risk Amelia might push down on Carter's injured legs.

"There aren't many pictures in this book," Carter explained.

"Yeah, Amelia. This is a chapter book." James added.

Carter flipped to an earlier title page showing the Hundred Acre Woods' crew. "Wow! I found a picture."

Carter turned the book to face Emily, James, and Amelia. Amelia stood up and started the rundown of the characters. "That's Piglet, That's Tigger."

"Who is that?" Emily asked pointing to Pooh.

James broke in, "Poopoo bear."

He broke out laughing and Carter let out a chuckle.

As the story continued, Christopher Robin sat down with his animal friends, encouraging them before an upcoming adventure.

Carter read, "You are braver than you believe, stronger than you seem, and smarter than you think."

That wrapped up the chapter and Carter closed the book and handed it to Emily.

"That was a good story," Carter said.

Amelia asked to see his hand. "You are stronger than you seem."

Carter caught Emily standing over their children and they exchanged a loving smile.

"Guys, I am so happy you came to visit. I will be coming home soon but will need lots of your help."

James shot the double thumbs up back at his father.

Looking at the bedside table, Carter remembered something.

"Doctor Z got you guys a little toy." Carter pointed to the counter where the sink was.

James and Amelia's eyes lit up at the three-letter t word.

Emily grabbed the pink and green spinners with the hospital logo as James attempted to pry them out of her hand.

"Please wait, James."

"I love you guys. Come on over here dude."

James approached Carter's outstretched fist.

"Knuckles, Daddy!"

Carter rubbed James' head.

"Princess Peach. You get over here."

Amelia hugged Carter's arm and blew a kiss.

"Emily, thank you. I can't say much more. This really made my day."

As Carter's family turned and walked out, he was determined to find more moments like that to fill his life with energy.

Yellow Light 11: Mindset matters and monitoring of your emotional energy is important.

TWELVE

· · · ● · ● · · ·

RANDALL PUCKERED HIS LIPS as he tried the Sour Patch Kids from the bag James had shared with him. "You have an incredible family, Carter."

"Thanks, Randall. Yeah, I am a lucky guy."

Carter dug into the bag of candy and found a fun size bag of Skittles.

Holding them up, "Randall, I remember you said these were your favorite. Want to trade?"

"Oh, yeah!"

Carter lobbed the bag onto Randall and Randall threw a KitKat bar to Carter in return. The exchange reminded Carter of the trading he used to do as a kid after emptying full pillowcases on the living room floor.

As Randall investigated the rest of the goodie bag, he began reading the newspaper.

Carter popped some M&Ms into his mouth and still garbling turned to Randall. "I have thought a lot about the advice vs. counsel thing and it got me thinking about a sales training I did earlier in my career around the power of the words you choose in conversations."

"What do you remember from it?" Randall asked.

"The main takeaway was the power of no and by positioning questions the right way on the delivery side you can make that response not be an option. Removing no as an option naturally prompts additional information being exchanged and the conversation expanding."

"Hmm...." Randall sighed. In his time driving the garbage truck, these business-type conversations weren't a daily occurrence.

Carter, now playing professor, continued, "Yeah... so if I ask questions with Who, What, Where, When, How, or Why, it's just not possible for the person on the other side to answer no."

"Okay," Randall responded.

"Yet it's more common in natural conversations to start questions with Can, Did, and Do. I think if I paired the focus on 'You vs. I' with knowing this difference too, it could change the strength of my relationships with everyone. But hey, what do I know."

"It might be the candy but I'm a little lost," Randall said smiling and trying to follow Carter's lesson.

"All right, here's a good example...Can I have another piece of your candy? What are your options for the response there?"

Not allowing Randall to reply, Carter jumped in. "In that scenario, it's yes or no."

"Okay, I am following more," Randall said, still half confused.

"Now think about this question. How would you feel about exchanging another piece?"

"Yeah, I definitely can't highlight my feelings with a yes or no."

"Exactly!" Carter exclaimed excitedly as his message got through to Randall. "The prior sales training taught me about avoiding closed-end questions. What the advice counsel thing has me thinking about is trying the other person's emotions and the YOU into questions as well. The first question you could just say No."

"That's good stuff, Carter Wilson."

"Yeah, man. There is lots of time to think here."

"For sure. Take a look at this photo."

Randall held up the newspaper. On the front page was a picture from a no-hands, pumpkin pie-eating contest.

"Such a shame to waste any pumpkin pie." Randall laughed. "Carla used to make the best pumpkin pie. I really miss it."

Carter was intrigued by Randall's life after the first evening of wisdom shared. At Randall's comment about Carla, Carter imagined how much harder things would be without Emily.

"How did you and Carla meet?"

"Oh, this is a great story. We met at a baptism party but one I wasn't invited to."

Carter chuckled. "Okay, how does that happen?"

"Carla's cousin that she grew up with had a daughter getting baptized. Her family had a party at a pavilion at Brookside Park. At the time, I was home from some military training and went to the park with one of my high school friends and his son. That kid was a nightmare and once he saw the large tiered cake, he wouldn't stop crying from the playground nearby and kept trying to run to the pavilion.

The ear piercing, 'I DON'T CARE IF IT'S NOT MINE. I WANT IT,' finally led to the most beautiful woman I have ever seen bringing a piece of cake over to the picnic bench where me and my friend were trying to calm down Little Mikey."

Carter laughed, "So you can thank Little Mikey?"

"For sure. That day he earned the nickname Cake, which I still call him today.

It gets better though. The cake exchange led to some of the kids from the party joining Little Mikey on the playground. The kids got along so well that my friend and one of the dads at the party exchanged numbers to meet up again. That is where I had to do a good amount of work and spend a few weekend mornings as the strange tag-along to the playground playdates until Carla came another time."

Carter smiled as he learned more about Randall.

"Wow, that's definitely a story that you can't forget. Nowadays, you probably could have seen her picture and found her on social media in a few seconds. I have a few friends that met their spouses that way."

Cindy came in right before 7:00 p.m. to let them know she was taking off but that R.J. was on the phone for Randall.

"I bet he's not coming." Randall sighed in frustration before picking up the bedside phone.

Randall picked up the line "Hey R.J., How are you?"

"Okay, okay, and Aunt Kim can get you from the bus station?"

"Yep. You can drive my car while home."

"Okay, love you, son, can't wait to see you."

Wheel of Fortune's first puzzle and intros played. Carter wasn't paying attention to the vowel bought and four As being revealed on the board. He watched Randall's eyebrows, waiting for him to look before asking him for an update.

"So that sounded like he is still coming. Right?"

"Yes, he's going to come tomorrow instead of Monday. He has an interview on Monday with a tech company in the city."

"Awesome! Hopefully, he can swing by and I can meet him. Maybe I can even help him prepare a bit."

Randall grabbed the Sunrise Senior Living folder. Randall knew the physical rehab to get back to his independence level would be challenging. Randall knew his preferred departure would be back to the three-bedroom ranch where he and Carla raised the boys.

It was a very active day for both Randall and Carter, from therapy to the kids dropping by, and the update on R.J. The sugar rush for Randall resulted in him conking out during the Double Jeopardy round, while Carter stayed awake.

Carter grabbed the notepad alongside the bed and started writing. He journaled about how his day went, what he looked forward to, and his concerns for the path ahead.

The notepad only had ten or so pages, so the margins ended up getting filled up, as Carter turned the page and wrote there as well. His understanding of how he needed to be more present for his family filled the final page. His writing was getting sloppy after an hour or so.

Holding his breath and blinking through tears, Carter remembered Emily's hand holding his when he woke up, and on his shoulder as he read Winnie the Pooh to the kids.

Carter looked down at the paper and reread the scribbled notes. He found that seeing his thoughts and feelings brought a new level of reflection. He found that the paper had more patience than people.

Yellow Light 12: Embrace each emotion and leverage journaling as a way for your deepest feelings and thoughts to be expressed.

THIRTEEN

· · · ● · ● · ● · ·

THE NEXT MORNING WAS Halloween. Good Morning America was already on the T.V. when Carter woke up. The cameras scanned the New York City tourists dressed in costumes, as the hosts wore witches' hats, fake mustaches, and animal ears.

Alexandra arrived alongside Cindy that morning.

"Boo!" Alexandra pulled the room divider startling Randall who had heard them enter the room but didn't catch that she had crept between the beds.

Cindy looked exhausted. "Happy Halloween, guys. Doctor Z is off today so Alexandra is going to lead the daily W.P.G. This is a big week for this room."

Alexandra erased the board from the prior day and wrote 'peace' as the word, 'courage' for the priority, and 'be seen' as her goal.

"My priority is 'selflessness' and goal, 'help others.'" Carter added.

Randall looked over at Carter. "Did they slip something into your veins overnight?"

Alexandra let out a giggle.

Carter was feeling different today, knowing his time in the hospital was limited, feeling repowered by the visit from the kids, and after the full notepad of content from the night before.

"Mr. Johnston, what about you?" Alexandra asked, looking over to Randall.

"My priority is 'interdependence' and my goal is 'planning my departure.'"

As Cindy stated upon her entry that morning, it WAS certainly going to be a big week for Room 205.

Randall asked. "What are your plans for Halloween?"

Cindy was the first to reply, "I am getting off a little early today and will be heading home to pass out candy."

"Nice, don't forget the leftovers for us." Randall smiled. "What about you Alexandra?"

Alexandra was taking Carter's blood pressure at the time and after finishing counting in her head she looked up Randall. "I'm not sure. We don't get many trick-or-treaters in my apartment complex. There is a costume party for the staff this evening that I might go to. Not sure yet.".

"What would you be going as?" Carter asked.

With a shrug of the shoulder, "Who knows? Maybe a cowgirl. I brought a hat and flannel in the car just in case I go."

"Just a reminder that your P.T. is right after lunch today," Cindy said as she left the room.

As the nurses left, Carter looked over at Randall, "You thinking what I am thinking? We got some work to do. Now that I know your skills with how you met Carla, I know you have it in you to help get John and Alexandra together at the party tonight."

With a mouth full of waffle, Randall laughed.

After a drink of water, Randall turned to Carter. "I really enjoy W.P.G. Peace is such a tough word." Off the cuff and at no prompt, Randall began another Yodaesque lesson.

"Having served in war, I can tell you that peace is what we are living at this very moment. What I found most challenging with society when I returned, which can still sometimes get me frustrated, is that we often continuously are waiting or rushing to find peace beyond the current moment."

"I find it hard to find peace with how busy I am." Carter shared.

Randall looked across at Carter. "Do you want me to tell you why you can't find peace?"

He also laughed knowing his knowledge about how to frame questions to avoid an option of no hadn't been fully understood by Randall.

"You left me open to say no based on how you asked that, but go ahead," Carter replied.

Randall began, "Peace directly conflicts with a fast-paced life. If you live in a world created by rush and hurry, you will never be happy in the moment. Rushing also brings out anger versus love. Your pause through this accident needs to be appreciated and now is the time to take small actions to realign yourself to match your future life with your desired values. This is an opportunity to find the peace and love that is so needed by you and by those in your life."

Carter took the Styrofoam coffee cup and held it close to his lips, eyes and ears fully on Randall. "I don't remember the last time I sat and just relaxed drinking a cup of coffee."

As a young worker returned to pick up the breakfast trays, Carter asked if he could get another notepad.

"What you got going there?" Randall said, pointing to the full pad.

"After last night, I started writing and it forced me to self-reflect. Before we had kids, I used to recap my days in a notebook before bed and dedicated time with Emily. I think I'm going to get back into it."

Carter spent the next few hours with the clean notebook, continuously looking up at the whiteboard.

'Selflessness' would be one of the last words that anyone who had met Carter in the past five years would use to describe him.

"So, Randall, I want to run something by you."

"Whatcha got Carter?"

Carter scooted up a bit in the bed. "Have you looked into any home healthcare agencies? If R.J. were to get this job locally and you were able to live at home and have a nurse come every so often, do you think you'd want that? I have a neighbor three houses down who runs a local office. When Emily calls, do you want me to get more information for you?"

Randall's priority of 'interdependence' was coming to life through the idea. Randall knew besides his hip and a few lingering health issues that he was in pretty good health for his age.

"Listen, it's something I would consider but I don't want anything happening with R.J. to influence my plan or his."

John arrived just at that moment to take Carter and Randall to physical therapy. Randall was asked to sit up and use his walker to get to the elevator. John had this planned. Alexandra was asked to wheel Carter down in the wheelchair.

After initial assisted stretching, John and a physical therapy assistant fitted crutches and Carter tried them out. He went around as Randall sat on a nearby table with ice on his hip, after the successful long walk to the elevator and P.T. area.

With the crutches under his armpits, Carter realized the physical strain and recovery from the crash was much more than just the healing needed for his leg. Despite the soreness in his ribs, it felt surprisingly great to feel his shoulder and arm muscles strain.

As John jumped between Carter and Randall, Randall said, "I heard there is a costume party later. Are you going?"

"Nah, I'll probably just head home, maybe go to the gym. I don't have a costume either." John replied.

Randall looked over at Carter and gave him a wink. "My go-to costume was always a flannel shirt tucked in, boots, and a bandana around my neck. Every man has that stuff laying around. You could be a modern-day cowboy."

Layering it on, "I remember when I was newer in my job, being present at those events always showed the higher-ups how invested you were in growing with the company."

Randall flashed a thumbs up to Carter, unseen to John who was facing Carter.

John seemed to appreciate Carter's comment about showing the higher-ups his commitment to the hospital.

"Yeah...That's kind of an easy costume. I think Max, the other physical therapist, said he was going to go. Maybe I'll swing home and grab that stuff during my lunch break after we wrap up."

"When does the party start?" Randall asked.

"At 6:00 p.m. There are like two shifts of the party, those that worked the day and those that work night so we don't leave you guys alone causing too much trouble."

"I hope you find yourself a nice cowgirl at the party," Randall said, smirking over to Carter.

Yellow Light 13: Peace conflicts with a fast-paced life.

FOURTEEN

· · · ● · · ● · ● · ·

AFTER A DAY OFF, Doctor Z returned to the hospital energized. Around 8:00 a.m., Doctor Z began his rounds on their floor.

He entered Room 205 and noticed the W.P.G. board. "Looks like the team had some really good thoughts yesterday. It's a big week for you guys."

"Yeah, today is a big day Doc, my son is coming home for fall break and Carter has a neighbor coming to talk about getting a home health aide vs. me going to Sunrise."

Doctor Z smiled, turned, and walked up to the whiteboard. "Instead of a word, I am going to substitute it with a number."

Doctor Z wrote '0.35%' in the area where the word of the day normally was placed. He followed up with his priority of 'time' and his goal of 'making effective decisions'.

Carter chose his priority as 'stretch' and his goal of 'embrace learning'. Randall added 'R.J.' as the priority and 'accept change' as his goal.

It had only been a handful of days since Carter was introduced to the W.P.G. model. What he had found to be impactful and important was seeing others' priorities and goals. This allowed him to better support and understand the other individual.

"All right gentleman, what do you think '0.35%' represents?" Doctor Z asked.

"No idea doctor, never been good with numbers. Ask the businessman." Randall replied with a laugh.

"Carter, any thoughts?"

"No idea," Carter replied.

"All right, so each day has 1,440 minutes. Five minutes each day is 0.35%. It's a short time but a lot can happen in five minutes. When I am down in the I.C.U., five minutes can be a matter of life and death. Time is the only consistent finite resource that we as humans deal with. Early on, my father taught me the principle of a five-minute favor. Here it is. Aim to spend five minutes each day doing something for someone else with no expectation of anything in return."

"That's pretty good," Carter said.

"It gets better but I am going to set a timer right now for five minutes and I want you both to sit in silence."

Doctor Z set the timer on his black wristwatch.

After about two minutes of silence, Randall and Carter exchanged a look, thinking the wristwatch would be beeping shortly. After another thirty seconds, Randall began thinking about how R.J.'s bus trip was going. Carter was thinking about needing to go to the bathroom.

The men heard some ambulance sirens outside pulling into the hospital, some muted conversations outside amongst the nurses, and even the heater kicking on.

After what felt like an hour, the wristwatch beeped.

"Funny how time can feel so long when asked to pause and listen." Doctor Z added.

"Just think about how much you both could accomplish in turning that time towards another person. What's even better is that it only represented 0.35% of your day."

Alexandra arrived.

"Good morning! How was the party?" Carter asked. The five minutes of silence left him eager to speak.

"Well Doctor Z showed up dressed as Dumbledore which made my costume subpar but John was there and was dressed like a cowboy which made it easy to talk to him. He said he got the idea from a patient earlier in the day."

Randall smirked. "That's funny, he mentioned he likely wasn't going to go and who would have thought you guys both went for the Western theme."

"As we talked, I learned he actually went to college with someone that I grew up with and was good friends with in high school. She is dating one of his friends and we are all going to get together next weekend."

Alexandra was bubbly as she talked about John.

"Wait, you guys aren't dating?" Doctor Z asked.

Alexandra was reluctant, knowing the policy around dating coworkers.

Sensing her hesitation, Doctor Z continued. "Alexandra, trust me, I know dozens of married couples that met across divisions here at the hospital. It just looked like you guys were really on the same page and I saw you walk out together."

Carter looked over at Randall, smirking about the work they did to make the interaction a bit easier for both John and Alexandra.

Looking to change the subject, Alexandra looked up at the board. "'0. 35%.' That's my favorite lesson I've learned here. It's funny the correlation with the number of decisions we make each day."

Randall and Carter looked a bit confused.

"You said it was your favorite, why don't you tell these guys why." Doctor Z asked.

"Of course, I will! It helped me in the first few weeks as I was getting settled in here at the hospital. It was all so new and I had to make a lot of decisions. Knowing this helped me make better ones." Alexandra replied.

"Adults make about 35,000 decisions each day. Most are subconscious or remotely conscious but adults make on average only 122 informed decisions each day. Which surprisingly also translates to 0.35%."

Out the window, the trees in the distance were now more bare than even a few days before and the heat was continuously kicking on and off in the hospital. It was hard to believe November was here, soon Thanksgiving, and then the holidays.

"So, Alexandra, that number there…0.35%…it seems pretty small but seems to tie to many important factors in each day."

"Yeah, it does. I mean admittedly the 35,000 decisions each day I didn't believe. But even the idea of breathing is I guess an uninformed decision. Regardless, it does put things into perspective a good bit and allowed me to trust my gut in the first few weeks and know that the ideas needing my most time and energy would be those 122 informed decisions."

Carter nodded and had to use his intellect a bit. He did some math in his head while looking a bit more.

"Yeah. If you are getting seven hours of sleep, that means over the course of the remaining seventeen hours, you are only making on average about seven informed decisions per hour."

Randall chimed in, "Why do you have to show off your quick math?"

Carter grunted as Randall gave an older generation's view.

"With the flood of information overload all the young ones get, that means the processing of the information to make those informed decisions is more important than ever. And I would bet Alexandra agrees with me that the 0.35% of informed decisions mean much more to our future than the thousands subconsciously made".

"Oh, absolutely!" Alexandra said.

Carter turned to his notepad to scratch down his takeaways from the W.P.G. session.

That morning Randall watched the news until physical therapy but did get up with his walker to go to the bathroom. Carter noticed him grab the Sunrise folder and toss it in the trash.

As 10:00 a.m. approached, Carter noticed John standing in the main hall talking to folks at the nurses' stand. His past visits were in and out.

"Hi, guys. Let's head on down." He said while entering the room.

Randall grabbed his walker and Carter was pushed down in a wheelchair by Cindy.

"See you later, Alex" John said while passing the nurses' stand turning to shadow Randall to the elevator.

"Randall, you are doing great with that walker. How does it feel?"

"My hip feels okay. I don't love the walker but I know it's necessary."

"Yes, it is, Mr. Johnston."

When the group arrived at the inpatient physical therapy area, John added some new strength exercises for both Randall and Carter.

As Randall worked with John, John reminded him. "These are things you will want to keep doing after you leave here Randall and don't get overconfident without a walker. I have seen too many folks your age making the mistake of thinking only a few steps to the kitchen won't do them any harm and then boom, they are back in the hospital again due to a fall."

"Do you think I will need it for the rest of my life?" Randall asked John.

"I can't give you an honest answer at this point. I have seen folks shift to a cane. If you ask me if I think you will run a marathon, I can tell you definitely no."

Carter laughed overhearing the comment to Randall.

"Carter, let's work today more with the crutches." John walked from Randall over to Carter.

Carter grabbed the crutches and was asked by John to head over to an area with two parallel wooden beams.

"Just like your crutches, hold these beams. We will wear this belt to hold you a bit more suspended but in the coming days will look to reduce that assistance. I also am confident that based on your strength, you could control pushing up with your arms to reduce the weight on your leg."

John mentioned this therapy was common for folks after a stroke or those with muscular dystrophy. Just a few weeks ago, Carter was running miles and golfing. Those thoughts flipped in his mind as he struggled to move forward along the beams.

The belt and John were still holding Carter so no pressure was felt. John asked Carter to gradually plant his feet onto the floor. Getting the uninjured left leg down was no issue but rolling from the tippy toe to heel and getting his right foot flat was a process that took Carter at least two minutes.

Carter slowly made his way fully across the fifteen-foot parallel beams, got some massage and heat, then he and Randall returned to the room.

Alexandra came down to get them instead of Cindy. John chose to walk behind Randall as well.

As Carter got back to Room 205 with Alexandra, they were surprised to see a young man sitting in the guest chair.

"Oh, sorry, they told me my dad was in this room." The young man said looking up from his phone.

"You're R.J., right?"

"Uh...Yeah."

"You are in the right spot. Your dad is right behind us. I am Carter. I've been sharing the room for the past week or so." Carter replied.

A relaxed wide grin from R.J. mirrored that of Randall.

"Nice to meet you, Carter."

Alexandra helped Carter from the wheelchair to the bed.

"Pops!

"Junior!"

"I was able to catch the earlier bus and got an Uber here," R.J. said, standing up as he saw his father shuffling into the room with the walker.

"R.J., I love you. Thank you for coming. They say it should be any day and I will be out of here."

R.J. watched his hero, his father, struggle around Carter's bed with his walker. R.J.'s mind was curious about what it would be like for his father once he was out of the hospital.

After sitting on the side of the bed, Randall turned to R.J., "So you got this big interview. Tell me more about it."

"So, it's with this tech company that works with the retail industry. They have been successful but have kind of plateaued. They plan to make some organizational shifts next year and although the day-to-day role isn't fully defined, it seems like I would be getting into a new division that they view as necessary for their next stage of growth." R.J. shared.

With the pride of a father, Randall looked for more details. "That sounds interesting. And they are located here?"

"Headquarters is downtown but they have offices in Chicago, San Francisco, and Austin, and want to open one in India."

Carter, being familiar with the space, chimed in. "Sorry for listening in, but I know the space well."

"Oh, you do?" R.J. asked.

"Yeah, lots of companies are tapping into the technical expertise and lower costs in India. Our company is planning to look there as well. I am happy to be a resource as you prepare for the interview. I've done a bunch of hiring in the past. I work for M.E.Z. and lead product strategy."

R.J.'s eyebrows shot up. "You said M.E.Z. right?"

"Yeah, started there on the ground floor, great spot."

Carter allowed Randall and R.J. to continue catching up.

Overhearing more about R.J.'s upcoming interview, Carter's mind started to race and accelerated when R.J. told his father the interview was with M.E.Z.

It had been less than two weeks but some of the plans R.J. shared seemed to highlight that progress was being made at M.E.Z. without him there. There were mixed emotions in learning this. Carter knew the medical leave would result in being away from the office for at least another two weeks and the lack of email traffic driving the day had admittedly been relaxing.

R.J. and Randall continued to catch up and chatted about how school was finishing up.

"Pops, what's the deal after you get out of here? You going to be good alone?"

R.J. was in the dark about the prior push from the hospital to send his father to Sunrise.

"So, the initial plan was to move into one of those senior living places but I really don't want to. I love the house, if I can get a ramp built in the front or better railings, it won't be a problem. I definitely shouldn't be doing the leaves anymore, so I will have to look into getting a neighborhood kid to do that and the shoveling."

Randall continued, "I've learned a lot about other options and know your generation does that grocery delivery thing to the house too. I realize it won't be like before but I feel there are years of my life where I could still live in our home."

"Listen Pops, I think that's a good idea. If I get the gig at M.E.Z., it would be smart for me to live at home a little and save up some money. I do know it's a hard job and long hours but you sacrificed a lot for me and I am happy to help if that makes your decision easier."

Carter could see off the window reflection, R.J. leaning to squeeze his father's hand and hug him.

"I told Aunt Kim I was on the earlier bus and she mentioned being in the area and able to pick me up. She texted me earlier that she would be coming around now. Do you mind if I head out with her and then I will come back tomorrow? I have to finish my final paper and prepare for this interview."

"Okay. Tell Kim I said hello and give her a hard time for getting sick last week and not coming to visit," Randall replied.

"Ha. I will. I love you, Pops!" R.J. smiled, letting go of his father's hand.

Randall smiled. "I am proud of you son. When you come back tomorrow, it seems like you might have an inside man that could help you learn more about M.E.Z."

R.J. shook Carter's hand as he left the room.

Both Randall and Carter sat in silence until it was interrupted by thunder outside.

The storm predicted on the morning news was whipping the trees around and bursts of heavy downpours left new visitors squeaking across the hallway tiles

"Carla used to hate the squeak of sneakers. I love it. It reminds me of the days coaching the boys' basketball at the Y.M.C.A."

"R.J. seems like a great kid."

That afternoon, Randall took a nap and Carter watched the news. There was a story of humanitarian efforts after a recent hurricane and a full thirty-minute broadcast by the local leader driving donation efforts. Within the cluttered notepad, Carter jotted down a goal to get back into volunteering more after he got out.

A few hours later after dinner, Emily arrived with their neighbor Kate. Kate's oldest daughter was James and Amelia's babysitter. She was short and heavyset, with dark curly hair. She was the first neighbor to greet the Wilsons with cookies when they moved onto Colts Court and was also quick to offer her daughter's babysitting services.

Before they entered the room, Carter was able to see Kate chatting it up with some folks at the nurses' desk.

"Hey Carter, you're looking good and I see they are taking good care of you. This place has changed a lot since I started my nursing career here twenty-three years ago."

She looked around the room and spotted the whiteboard, alongside drawings from James and Amelia.

"Ah...They must be carrying on Doctor Jones' old W.P.G. program. I remember '0.35%.' That's a really good one."

Kate and Emily squeaked across the floor in their rain boots as Randall waved.

"And you must be Randall," Kate said in a welcoming tone as she walked toward the middle of the room.

"That's me. Hopefully, Emily said nice things." Randall smiled at Emily who was standing behind Kate.

Randall jumped right into conversation with Kate. "Carter gave me some nuggets to think about and I really don't want to go into that nursing home so I look forward to hearing more about what you might be able to share about the homecare."

Kate set her umbrella along the side of the wall. "Let me get settled and I can tell you all about the options. We have partnerships with hospitals. Your therapies can be done at home. Sometimes we can send people to help with things like laundry and meals. Lots of options to chat about."

Randall knew the continued therapy could be beneficial along with some help getting daily tasks done. He liked the idea of having some company and Kate could already tell he was a talker that would benefit as much from the care as the social interaction.

"Carter, I'm going to chat more with Randall in a bit more privacy." Kate shut the divider as Emily and Carter chatted about the latest with the kids.

"So, Randall, the nurses said you broke your hip. How did that happen?"

Kate went through what seemed like a scripted list of questions to evaluate Randall's qualifications for homecare.

"As a veteran and on Medicare, we could easily get someone there for twenty-five hours a week. The folks could plan to come from 10:00 a.m. - 2:30 p.m. There are a good number of nurses that love those hours because they can see their family off to school and return home by the time the bus drops off. That's actually what I did initially when I shifted from the hospital to home health before getting a leadership role managing the office."

Kate left the room and brought Alexandra into the session with Randall. As Alexandra left, she opened the divider. Kate stepped back to sit alongside Emily.

"Emily, just a reminder that we gotta get going so I can get to pick up from volleyball."

Emily looked down at her watch. She knew Kate's daughter was going to need to be picked up.

Kate grabbed her umbrella and stood by the door. Now pointing to Randall. "I will have to talk with the broader nursing team to understand your discharge timing and needs but I will get the wheels in motion with your insurance and V.A. to give you a better sense of how it will all work."

Randall winked over at Carter as the women gathered their things to leave. "Thank you, Carter."

Yellow Light 14: Build a comprehension of 0.35%. The five minutes dedicated to others and the focus on 0.35% of your daily decisions being informed will transform your life.

FIFTEEN

· · ● · ● · ● · ● · ·

RANDALL'S FINAL DAYS IN the hospital flew by. Kate dropped by another time to confirm some of the discharge logistics and to introduce Randall to a few members of her staff that might be filling the first shifts after he got out.

The weekend get-together with John and Alexandra's mutual friends led to the two staying up talking until 2:00 a.m. John's time around the nurse stand seemed to get longer and longer each trip back and forth with patients for physical therapy.

Randall's final scheduled day in the hospital arrived. The discharge was planned for 1:00 p.m. By 7:00 a.m., Randall had finished about twenty laps around the floor with his walker.

Carter woke up to the T.V. on but Randall was not in the bed. Looking into the hallway, Carter noticed Randall rounding the corner with his walker, wide grin, and haircut and shave from the night before.

Randall waved and decided to head into the room to spend some final minutes with Carter.

Alexandra followed behind.

"Today is the big day Mr. Johnston. I spoke to Kate. She mentioned the home aide will meet you this afternoon at the house and R.J. will be coming with your sister Kim to pick you up."

Alexandra waved to Carter and wiped the prior day's board, writing the word 'YET' in all caps.

"Carter, I am going to have you guys start with goals and priorities then I will do mine."

Carter was honestly a little emotional knowing Randall would be leaving, despite knowing that Emily was planning to swing by with the kids for dinner.

"My priority is 'improvement' and my priority is 'to live by lessons learned,'" said Carter.

Alexandra then turned to Randall who was sitting in the guest chair alongside his bed.

"'Thankfulness' and 'stay the course.'"

Alexandra tapped the marker against the board, thinking how just a few days before this exercise was like pulling teeth.

Mid-whiteboard session, there was a knock on the door, John entered with an extra coffee cup in hand.

"Good morning, Alex. Here is a cup of the Colombian blend you were raving about. Have a great day!"

Alexandra started towards John, both arms moving away from her side ready to embrace John. She caught herself as Carter and Randall shared a smirk.

"John, that is so sweet of you. Just a reminder that Randall will be out of here so you won't see him this afternoon," she said.

"Oh, I know. Only one pain in the butt from Room 205 for a few more days." John looked in the room at Carter and Randall. "Mr. Johnston, it was a pleasure meeting you and I'm happy to hear that you will be heading home instead of Sunrise. I don't know who will replace you as my inside informant to Carter's frustrations about his P.T. progress." John chuckled, nodded to Alexandra, and turned to the elevator.

Alexandra turned to the board and wrote her priority and goal, 'love' and 'embrace the future'.

"That love is about how heartbroken you are about me leaving, right?" Randall asked with a smile.

"Of course, Randall."

After Alexandra left, Carter said, "Randall, I am honestly going to miss you. Can you write down your phone number and address so that once I am out maybe we can grab food?"

Randall grabbed his own notepad and ripped off the page with his phone number.

The breakfast arrived and Doctor Z stopped in to wish Randall good luck. Doctor Z looked up at the board in an attempt to share some final wisdom for Randall to take.

"'YET"...such a damn good word. It opens up the world of possibility and promotes an open mind and an awareness of the future. After every statement, just add that word and see what it does to your thinking." Doctor Z shook Randall's hand and headed out the door.

Knowing he was leaving today Randall had already had Alexandra help tidy up his side of the room and the bag of personal stuff built up during his stay at the hospital.

Carter and Randall spent the morning talking about the past few days and although Randall wasn't slotted to leave until 1:00 p.m., R.J. and Aunt Kim arrived around 11:45 a.m.

"You must be Carter," Kim said after nodding across to Randall who was embracing R.J. with a hug.

"Yes, I am. It's nice to meet you. Randall has told me a lot about your family and how much he loves his baby sister."

Kim blushed, "Oh dear, Randall and his stories."

"R.J., how'd the interview go?" Carter asked.

"It went really well. I did two by phone before this one. From what I read online, they normally do this one in-person and one final call by phone."

Carter had the inside scoop on M.E.Z.'s hiring process.

"I met with the C.E.O. and Director of HR. From what I understand, they will be looking to place a Chief People Officer above the role that I am applying for but mentioned it will be another senior person internally. I just got an email last night for the final call to take place in two days."

Carter knew this meant R.J. would be getting the job and he was going to ask Emily to let him send an email to the hiring team to put in a good word.

"That's awesome and a good sign." Carter knew it was a sure bet the offer would come.

"Yeah. We'll see."

"If I can help at all, please feel free to call me at the hospital."

"Honestly, some of the lack of structure is unsettling and I was considering looking to leave the area but the numbers floated during the in-person meeting were pretty darn compelling when looking at the cost of living here vs. the other cities I have interviewed."

R.J. was thinking clearly about this and recognized the impact the decision would play. "You've been there a while, what do you think?"

Carter was eager to jump into providing advice but paused before replying and shifting to counsel. "This is a decision only you can make. What do you want from a first professional job?"

"I really don't know."

"That's totally normal. It's a huge decision. Here are a few things to think about. How do the known fears of the role make you feel? To what extent would your impact be felt at M.E.Z. vs. other places you are considering?"

Randall lifted the baseball cap off his head and stroked his hair while nodding to the questions.

Carter sensed some anxiousness. "M.E.Z. has been great for me. I understand why they are investing in the division that you would be a key part of shaping."

Carter continued, "Here are my final suggestions, write down the questions you haven't had answered and bring them to that final discussion. Vulnerability around uncertainty is an important leadership quality."

"Thanks, Carter." R.J. shook Carter's hand.

Kim and Randall looked towards R.J., both proud of knowing how bright the future would be.

Randall stood up and went into the hallway, his fleece jacket now on.

After two laps, Alexandra saw him and headed into Room 205 as Randall continued his walker marathon.

"Kim, R.J., he won't be able to leave until 1:00 p.m. He needs to have a final clearance from the doctor. I know he's eager to go but I don't think anyone wants him to be doing laps for the next hour or so."

Kim headed out of the room to catch up with her big brother.

"Randall, just come on to the room. We can't leave for an hour. Enjoy the time with Carter."

With nudges in the final quarter of the lap, Randall headed back to Room 205 and ordered his final lunch, a buffalo chicken wrap.

The full care team arrived at the room after lunch. Doctor Z, Cindy, Alexandra, and John all gave Randall final reminders as Kim headed downstairs to grab the car.

Justin, the man who supported Carter up from the I.C.U. stood by the door with a wheelchair. Although Randall was stable walking with the walker, it was hospital protocol for him to be wheeled out the door. R.J. folded up the walker and held it under his arm

Randall shook the staff members' hands and pointed to Carter. "You have a lot of life to live. You have not lived as your best self...YET."

Yellow Light 15: 'Yet' encourages confidence and makes anything a possibility.

Sixteen

· · · · · · · · · ·

It felt like only minutes after Randall left that a hospital employee came into Room 205. The worker wiped Randall's name off the whiteboard and stripped the sheets.

Carter noticed a small piece of Skittles wrapper fall between the beds.

The T.V. that normally played in the background was a blank black screen. Feeling a wave of emotions, Carter grabbed the notepad from the side table.

Carter hit the final page in the pad before flipping it over and continuing to document the lessons he learned from Randall. The sound of a familiar voice made Carter raise his eyes to the wall clock.

"No, Amelia! That's mine."

Emily arrived at the doorway, James and Amelia behind playing tug-o-war with a Super Mario figurine.

Leaving Room 207, Alexandra joked as the kids fought in the hallway.

"James, Amelia, you won't believe what happened?"

"What happened?" the kids said in unison.

"Mario, Princess Peach, and Yoshi came to visit your dad a few days ago."

Amelia looked up with a confused look.

"Nice try. That was us, silly!" James replied while ripping his arm down and winning the tug-o-war battle.

James hopped into the room. "Hey Daddio"

"What's up bud?" Carter said, giving James a high five.

After a few screams of frustration, Amelia followed into the room. Amelia immediately noticed the bed sheets were off Randall's bed.

"Is that old man in heaven?"

Carter smiled, "No sweetie, he got out earlier today, and you know Ms. Kate from down the road?"

Amelia nodded her head.

"Ms. Kate has nurses that will be coming to Randall's house to continue taking care of him. Maybe we can all go visit him. Would you like that?"

"Yes." James and Amelia responded in unison.

Emily kissed Carter and placed the McDonald's bag on the windowsill.

"Mommy, can I please have the Happy Meal toy?" James asked.

"Be patient please."

"I got four Happy Meal toys this week. That's like a zillion times more than I got all last year."

Emily pulled the guest chairs together and brought the meal tray in front of Amelia and James.

"You know the rules, you have to eat the chicken nuggets first," Emily said as she set down the bags.

Amelia let out a humph and folded her arms.

Emily turned her attention to Carter.

"So, any updates on your exit?"

"Still on track to leave in two days. They are thinking in the morning. John has given me a bunch of exercises to do daily but I will need to continue physical therapy in the outpatient area for another two months, at least.

They want me to do it at the hospital outpatient area for another week or two then I can look to find another location closer to the office or home."

Emily nodded as Carter went on, "I actually already set it up for Wednesday and Saturday mornings those two weeks.

I thought about your work schedule and my parents' normal weekly plans. My mom should be able to bring me Wednesday and Saturday we are normally this way for James' soccer."

"Seems like your planning brain is working again too. Thank you for considering my work schedule. Just a reminder, your medical leave still goes another two weeks but Nancy did say that you can ride with her to the office when you are ready to go back."

Amelia and James had gobbled up the chicken nuggets. Only one ended up on the floor.

"Mommy, can I please have the toy?" Amelia asked, holding up the empty nugget box.

Thankfully, McDonald's helped Emily, like so many parents, and had the same toy in James and Amelia's box.

"Here you go." Emily ripped off the plastic and handed each kid their toy.

"It's Mr. Incredible!" James screamed.

James had seen the movie a while back. Emily caught glimpses of the movie but Carter hadn't even heard of it.

"This should be our Halloween costumes next year!" James said excitedly. "Daddy, you can be Mr. Incredible, I can be Dash, Amelia can be Violet, and Mommy can be Elastigirl."

"Great idea buddy." Carter only knew the name of the character and felt he had a lot to live up to if he was going to be Mr. Incredible.

Alexandra knocked on the door and waved goodbye for the evening. Over her shoulder, Carter noticed John waiting by the nurses' stand with a bunch of flowers.

Emily got out of her chair. "Hey, Alexandra?"

"Yes?"

"Will you be here when Carter leaves?" Emily had grown fond of Alexandra and the patience she had shown Carter.

"I am off tomorrow but come in early the next day so I should be around," Alexandra said looking down at her watch.

"James and Amelia, you take care of your Daddy when he is out of here."

"We will!" James said, smiling back.

After Emily and the kids left, Carter turned on the T.V. to watch Wheel of Fortune and Jeopardy alone. He hoped Randall's transition back home went smoothly and wondered if he was watching too.

The hospital notepads had filled up over the past few days and Carter spent the evening reading and consolidating takeaways. The index card that Doctor Z gave him when he left the I.C.U. also sat in the pile and was incorporated into what Carter coined, 'Yellow Lights for Progress'.

<u>Yellow Lights for Progress</u>

1. Pause and look around.

2. Understand what got you to this moment.

3. Show you care by not allowing others to share only one-word responses.

4. There is no step-by-step guide to life.

5. Appreciate the interconnectivity of others.

6. Never underestimate the joy you can find in time with a stranger.

7. Share goals with and for others and accept progress and movement are different things.

8. Keep your eyes forward and know that sometimes pedal to the floor is not an option.

9. A key to authenticity is vulnerability.

10. Understand the difference between advice and counsel.

11. Mindset matters and monitoring of your emotional energy is important.

12. Embrace each emotion and leverage journaling as a way for your deepest feelings and thoughts to be expressed.

13. Peace conflicts with a fast-paced life.

14. Build a comprehension of 0.35%. The five minutes dedicated to others and the focus on 0.35% of your daily decisions being informed will transform your life.

15. 'Yet' encourages confidence and makes anything a possibility.

SEVENTEEN

· · • · • · • · •

CARTER'S FINAL FULL DAY at the hospital started a bit differently. Normally the morning news was on the T.V. and Randall was ready to play reporter before Carter's eyes were even open.

Cindy dropped by, as Alexandra had the day off.

"Good morning, Carter. You must be excited about tomorrow."

"Yes, I am. How is your mother doing?" Carter asked with genuine interest and with an expanded appreciation built over the last few weeks in taking interest in others.

"Thank you for asking. She is doing better and we have her receiving some help from a memory care group. Last night she forgot who my husband was but as I gave her a hug leaving, she said 'My little girl. I love you."

"Would you like the pancakes or oatmeal today?" Cindy asked

"Would it be possible to get both?" Carter asked.

Cindy tidied up some of the sheets of the notepad that had fallen onto the floor. "Absolutely dear."

Cindy held one page of the notepad, examining it thoroughly.

"What is this?"

"Uh...just some lessons I learned through this experience and that I want to make sure to incorporate into my life after I leave," Carter replied, a bit uneasy as he saw her reading through.

"Can I make a copy of this?" Cindy asked.

"I guess so."

Was there really anything that good on that list? Carter sat staring at the W.P.G. board on the wall ahead.

Cindy left with the chicken-scratched page and returned shortly with the original page and a handful of extra copies.

"Here you go. Thanks for letting me copy that. The one about monitoring emotional energy hit me hard."

"Yeah. I started writing the past few days."

"Carter, I like the person you are now a lot more than the a-hole that we were warned about when you got to this floor," Cindy smirked at Carter. "Just a reminder, you have a round of tests before your final session with John in the middle of the day."

"I appreciate you. Thanks for everything."

The same tests Carter would be having in a few hours wiped him out for a full afternoon just a few days before.

As Carter ate the oatmeal, he thought about the hidden blessings that came through his time at the hospital. Could the 'Yellow Lights for Progress' be something he could put into action?

A few more pages of the notepad were filled out before Carter was wheeled down for the tests.

The tests lasted about forty-five minutes. Carter was asked to move his legs in directions and ways that were unnatural, even to someone that hadn't just had major surgery.

With no break from being twisted and turned, Carter continued to his final session with John. John ran through every exercise he did with Carter during his in-patient daily physical therapy.

"Carter, I got you signed up for two days a week. I would ideally want to see you three or four days, but I know you have a lot on your plate. I am trusting that you will do at least these three exercises daily."

John circled three pictures of exercises from the stapled packet of five, full pages which covered everything they did together.

"John, you've got a skill here. It has been a pleasure working with you."

"Carter, it's been great working with you. I will see you in just a few days. I owe you and Randall for the set-up with Alex."

"Ha. Never underestimate the joy you can find in time with a stranger."

The men shook hands as John's next patient arrived. Carter reached into the pocket on the left side of the wheelchair and gave John a copy of 'Yellow Lights for Progress' in exchange for the exercise packet.

"The whole group here taught me a lot. I thought this list could accompany the W.P.G. framework Doctor Z has implemented." Carter smiled, handing the copy over to John.

John looked through the list, nodding as he scrolled the twice-folded paper.

"Any of them standing out to you?" Carter asked.

"Never underestimate the joy you can find in time with a stranger. You just said that to me."

"Well, I wouldn't call Alex a stranger anymore," Carter said laughing as a young volunteer arrived behind the wheelchair to bring him up to Room 205 one last time.

"Thank you again, John. I will see you next week."

As Carter arrived, Doctor Z was sitting in the guest chair looking out the window. Doctor Z turned slowly, wiping his eyes with the sleeve of his shirt before looking up at Carter.

"Everything alright Doc?"

"Not really. It's another year and it doesn't get easier. This is the first year I am working. Just trying to see if being distracted more helps at all. My wife is a mess. I just wish Kyle was still with us."

Doctor Z closed his eyes tightly. Carter could see Doctor Z's shoulder move up and down as he breathed deeply.

"Do you want to talk more about Kyle? I heard he was one hell of a ball player." Carter said, looking to lighten the mood a bit.

"He was, but an even better son. I just wish we could have caught the infection sooner and helped him," Doctor Z said through held-back tears.

"I knew you were down with John and Randall took off and this would be a quiet room for a few minutes." Doctor Z stood up slowly and headed towards the door.

Carter grabbed the spare copies of 'Yellow Lights for Progress' that lay on the bedside tray.

"Doc, before you go, I want to give you something." Carter handed an extra copy over to Doctor Z.

Doctor Z pulled his glasses out of his pocket and sat down again, diving into the content Carter had consolidated over his stay.

"Thanks for sharing this. It's rewarding to see you embracing some of what we strive to teach here. Just remember, your future is not to be written by words, but instead by actions. I will be back tomorrow for your send-off."

Eighteen

· · · · • · • · · ·

CARTER STRUGGLED TO SLEEP the final night in the hospital. After Jeopardy and Wheel of Fortune, Carter started writing on another small notepad.

The final words of the evening. Don't hit the gas at the yellow light.

Carter woke up around 6:15 a.m. and turned on the morning news. The weather anchor was outside of a Christmas farm that was opening that weekend.

Bundled up in a peacoat, scarf, leather gloves, and ear muffs, the reporter mentioned a high for the day of thirty-three degrees and flurries later in the week.

The shift from the overnight to day crew happened at 7:00 a.m. and Carter saw Alexandra walk in with her coffee cup in hand.

Carter waited patiently and, like clockwork, Alexandra dropped in around 7:05 a.m. As someone equally appreciative of timeliness, her punctuality made him feel well cared for.

The five minutes helped him turn back to the 'Yellow Lights for Progress' he had in hand to share with Alexandra.

"Carter, I thought you would like to hear that John asked me on another date next weekend." Alexandra smiled cheerfully.

"We were also talking last night about the coincidence of wearing the same costumes...I should have known you guys had something to do with it." Alexandra said, doing a quick scan of Carter's vitals.

Carter laughed, shrugging with an innocent twinkle before tapping his nose with his finger.

Alexandra returned shortly with oatmeal, pancakes, and coffee, setting in on the bedside tray, and shifting Carter's papers to the guest chair.

"Take one." Carter motioned, pointing to the copies Cindy made.

"You put this together?"

Carter nodded.

"I just saw it posted on the whiteboard of the nurses' stand."

Carter couldn't help but feel as proud as a toddler with their artwork on the fridge.

"Yeah, it wasn't until I was forced to pause that I realized my priorities were out of whack and I was missing so many good moments." Carter looked down at the final two copies and the original.

"I will be back once Doctor Z gets in." Alexandra turned and left the room.

A few minutes later, Emily rang in.

"Hey babe, is everything still on track?"

Carter heard the kids fighting in the backseats.

"I believe so, Doctor Z should be arriving soon and I've already seen Alexandra."

"Awesome! We are looking forward to having you home. I will be there in about forty minutes. We've missed you." Emily hung up.

The idea of going home flooded Carter with emotions.

I need to do better in embracing every moment. I don't want to have to experience such a long pause any time soon to get back to my true self. Emily and the kids deserve my best.

Doctor Z come by with Alexandra. "So... Carter Wilson, today is the day."

Doctor Z went to the whiteboard, erasing yesterday's W.P.G., and wrote 'revived'. He continued with the goal of 'discipline' and priority of 'carry it forward.'

As Doctor Z turned to Carter and Alexandra, James ran through the door.

"Daddy! We are breaking you out of here."

"Buddy. We still have a few things we have to do." Carter looked up, seeing Emily carrying Amelia.

Shuffling into the room, Emily put Amelia on the guest chair.

"Amelia, you have to make some room for your brother."

"No! I want to go home."

James stood next to Carter. "Amelia is grumpy. She fell asleep in the car and mommy had to wake her up."

Doctor Z reached into his pocket and pulled out a fidget spinner. "James, can you bring this over to your sister and share the chair and this."

After the disruption, Doctor Z chose to stand behind the kids and monitor the toy-sharing situation.

"Alexandra, do you mind closing this whiteboard session out?"

"Sure thing. I will add mine."

Alexandra and Doctor Z did a handoff of the marker Alexandra added 'Appreciation' to her goal and 'Stay connected'.

With only one spot left on the board for goals and priorities, Carter jumped in. "I know Alexandra and Doctor Z already saw this sheet." Carter grabbed a copy and handed it to Emily.

"I was always selfish in the past. My goals and priorities were always put ahead of others. I want Emily to fill the final spots."

Emily had been involved in the sessions in the past and knew the patient's input was always incorporated in the past.

"Doctor Z, is this a step you are okay with?" Emily asked.

"As Carter's list says, there is no step-by-step guide to life. Carter's priorities are shifting in the right direction. Go ahead, Emily."

Doctor Z smiled while keeping an eye on James and Amelia.

"All right, Alexandra. 'Grateful' and 'prepare for goodness ahead.'"

After a run-down of paperwork, Emily, James, and Amelia headed down with Alexandra to the pick-up area.

Alexandra hugged Carter. "Thank you! You better take all these things you say you've learned and put them into practice. I will make sure John keeps you honest and asks you about it when you come back in the next few weeks."

Doctor Z and Carter were the only ones left in the room. Doctor Z looked Carter directly in the eyes.

"Live by those principles that you put together. I will incorporate them into my own work here if you promise me to be the true champion of these. Remember, words must be backed up by action. You asked for a step-by-step guide when I first met you. You created that for yourself."

His eyes closed and after four or five nods, Carter opened his eyes.

"Thank you, Doctor Z. I never would have wished this accident to happen but I feel it needed to happen to reset where things were going."

Doctor Z patted Carter on the shoulder. "You take care of yourself, my friend."

Carter was wheeled out of the hospital to his family waiting curbside.

NINETEEN

· · · ● · ● · ● · ·

CARTER GRASPED EMILY'S HAND as they crossed town.

At the second stoplight, Carter noticed a bakery and coffee shop. It was the spot Alexandra grabbed her morning Colombian blend.

"Want to swing in there?" Carter said, pointing to the coffee shop.

"Sure, but it looks like the drive-thru is packed."

"That's okay. We are not in a rush."

Carter and Emily were five cars from ordering. Carter looked into the rearview mirror to see Amelia already dozing off.

James' eyes met Carter's in the mirror and James smiled.

"I missed you, Daddy."

"I missed you too buddy. Do you want to get a hot chocolate?"

"Oh yes! And don't forget, we have to get Amelia one too."

Now only two cars in front of them, Carter looked to the right and saw his M.E.Z. colleague, Natalie. Carter put his window down. The cold November air started to fill the car.

"Natalie!"

"Carter! How are you feeling?"

"Still a long road ahead. My daughter is sleeping in the back." Carter rubbed his hands together, signaling he needed to close the window.

"See you soon."

Emily pulled up to place the order.

A woman's voice greeted them. "Welcome to Grounded, what can I get for you?"

"Two hot chocolates, a small dark roast...Carter, you want the iced coffee?"

Yelling across from the passenger's seat, Carter chimed in, "Make it two small dark roasts."

With drinks in tow, the Wilsons continued home. Amelia was peacefully asleep, James sipping a hot chocolate, and Emily and Carter holding hands.

Pulling into the driveway, there was a large banner across the garage door where Carter normally parked his Jeep. The banner read, 'Welcome Home Daddy!'

Carter's eyes filled with tears. Carter could hear Zeus barking from the driveway. Emily carried Amelia into the house and set her on the couch. James headed in and started drawing on his dinosaur coloring book. Emily returned to help Carter out of the S.U.V., handing crutches to her husband. Carter made his way through the garage.

Upon entering the kitchen, Zeus clawed at his cage, eager to see his fetch partner back.

Two laundry baskets were sitting in the kitchen and dishes pilled over the lip of the sink. Emily walked in behind Carter, carrying the bags from the hospital.

"I am sorry the house is a mess. I tried to find time last night but fell asleep reading to James."

Carter looked at Emily. "Everything looks perfect. And you look beautiful. This mess is simply a sign that we are living the life we chose together."

"I love you. I have to run out and get one last bag."

As Emily headed through the garage she saw their neighbor Kate walking her dog.

"Hey, Emily. Is Carter home now?"

"We just got home."

Kate could see Emily was both relieved but also ready to get back inside from the cold.

"That's great." Reaching into her pocket, Kate continued. "I was going to put this in your mailbox. It's from Randall for Carter."

Kate handed Emily a folded envelope. Despite the eagerness to open it up and read it right then Emily grabbed it.

"Thank you, Kate. You have been a tremendous help these last few weeks. I owe you."

"Emily, you don't owe me a thing. This is what neighbors are for. If you need anything, let me know."

TWENTY

· · • · • · • · • · ·

NORMALLY BEING OUT OF the house before the rest of the family was awake, Carter wasn't exposed to the true chaos that filled the house on normal weekday mornings.

With medical leave slotted for another week and a half, Carter embraced the time at home.

The second night home, Carter offered to help Emily with bath time. The kids raced upstairs to the hallway bathroom between their two rooms. Carter's journey up the stairs took a long time because of the crutches.

Carter limited his ups and downs throughout the day and still needed to stop on the middle landing before tackling the final six steps up. Emily walked behind Carter to make sure he didn't fall or need support while going up. The three-step practice stairs used during physical therapy didn't get him too prepared for the full flight.

James and Amelia were jumping and dancing in the bathroom when Carter and Emily reached the top.

James had picked up some bathroom words from riding the school bus and Amelia got a kick out of stepping in and out of the bathroom doorframe, screaming 'diarrhea' and 'poopy butt'.

James started the nighttime routine by getting the toothbrushes out of the medicine cabinet on the wall and helped Amelia put the toothpaste onto her Cinderella brush.

"Daddy, I like you helping with bath time," Amelia said, smiling into the mirror with toothpaste on her chin and one arm out of her sweatshirt.

"Me too!" James yelled as he hopped off the footstool and started to get undressed.

While James hopped into the bathtub, Carter sat with Amelia reading.

It was about 7:15 p.m. as the showers wrapped up. James got himself dressed into pajamas. Emily helped Amelia get dressed.

"Hey Emily, I saw that Jeopardy is bringing back Teen Week. I think it starts tonight, what do you think about watching it as a family? It starts in like ten minutes."

"Sure! I know you got into it when you were at the hospital and I think Grandpa and James watched one night when the kids were there." Emily replied.

Running from his room to Amelia's, James danced in the hallway.

"Oh, yeah! We get to stay up all night."

Amelia had a late nap, so staying up would help get her to fall asleep faster after the show.

James was smacking his butt and jumping up and down as Amelia cracked up at her big brother's dancing.

James finally settled down and turned to his parents. "Daddy, when I watched it at Gram and Grandpa's there was a question where the answer was a paleontologist and I got it right!"

Emily and Carter laughed as the family made their way downstairs. Zeus sat behind the gate as the Wilsons entered the back area of the house. After Final Jeopardy, Carter noticed Amelia had fallen asleep in Emily's arms. Carter's shirt was wet from where James snuggled into him with wet hair from the shower. Emily turned off the T.V. and looked over to James and Carter.

"I am going to carry Amelia up to bed. James, why don't you head up to your room and I will be in there soon."

"Goodnight Daddy," James said, giving Carter a big hug. James smiled and made his way to his room.

TWENTY-ONE

· · · · ●· · ●· · ·

THE NEXT MORNING, CARTER woke up to Amelia sneaking into her parents' bedroom. Amelia bumped Carter's brace as she navigated from the base of the bed to between her parents.

Carter was always out before this common morning guest arrived as part of Emily's wake-up routine.

"Amelia, can you please show Daddy how you get dressed by yourself?"

As quickly as Amelia scooted into the bed, she shuffled out of the room.

Carter looked over to Emily. "What time is it?"

Rubbing her eyes Emily replied, "About 5:30 a.m."

"Why don't you take the time to shower and I can bring Amelia downstairs."

"Are you sure? Normally she wants to eat right away and Zeus will want to go out."

As much as Carter wanted to give Emily time, he realized quickly that driving these steps of the morning routine would be challenging with his crutches.

"I can probably get her food. Do you think Zeus can wait until you come down?"

"He should be fine."

Grasping the first crutch leaning against the nightstand, Carter knew things were likely to only become more challenging the next few weeks as the entire family adjusted to him being home and moving at a different pace.

By the time Carter made his way across the bedroom, Amelia was standing in the doorway holding her socks in her hand.

"Daddy, can you help me put these on? Mommy always does."

After a deep breath, "Amelia, let's head downstairs and we can do it down there."

Zeus began whimpering from his cage as soon as he heard Amelia begin bouncing down the stairs.

"Daddy, I want Cheerios. I can get them myself if you get me the milk."

Amelia grabbed a bowl from the lower cabinet filled with the kids' bowls and cups as well as the box of Cheerios in the pantry and sat at the table.

Managing to only spill a few Cheerios, Amelia straightened in her seat, pride shining in her eyes.

"Daddy, I am ready for the milk."

Carter curled the milk jug in his ring and pinky finger as the rest of his hand stayed secure to the crutch.

"Here you go, baby."

Looking up at her father, "I love you, Daddy!"

"I love you too."

As Carter returned to the fridge, he noticed a folded-up note on the island with his name on it. He didn't recognize the handwriting.

Unfolding the paper, Carter read:

Carter

I hope Kate was able to get this to you and you are settling in at home. Give me a call, I'd like to get together.

Randall

930-3735

Emily arrived a few minutes later and headed over to take care of Zeus.

"Good Morning Amelia."

"Hi, Mommy!"

Emily noticed Carter holding the note from Randall.

"I saw Kate yesterday. She said Randall is doing well but wanted to try to get together soon."

Knowing that Randall always was awake early when he was at the hospital, Carter asked Emily for her phone and dialed Randall.

After five or so rings, the answering machine message went off with a woman's voice, "You've reached the Johnstons, we can't come to the phone right now. Leave a message and we will get back to you as soon as possible."

Carter listened to Carla's voice and sat with the reference to 'we' still present in the automated message.

"Hey Randall, It's Carter Wilson. I got the note…"

Randall must have made his way to the machine at this time, as it cut off and he hopped onto the line.

"Carter! Good morning. Sorry, I didn't get to the phone in time."

"No problem. I know you are an old man." Carter laughed. "So…how have you been?"

Unable to get in many words, Randall's excitement was felt through the phone.

"R.J. helped me get set up with Netflix and one of the aides got me hooked on this new show about the Marines training. It makes my stretching and rehab exercises a joke."

"I am happy to hear things are going so well." Carter listened on as James arrived in the kitchen.

Hearing the background noise and sensing some increased distraction, "Carter, do you want to give me a call later today instead?"

"No, we are good. I just can't move to a quieter space."

Randall smiled on the other side of the phone. "I get it. Are you and the family able to meet soon for breakfast? It will be on me. I owe you for getting me connected with Kate."

"Let me chat with Emily. I won't get any approval to drive for a few weeks."

Randall and Carter sat in silence for about ten seconds.

Carter broke the silence. "As good as it is to be home, I have to be honest, I hate feeling dependent on others."

Randall was quick to reply. "Life is about building your community of people you can be dependent on."

Twenty-Two

· · • · • · • • · ·

The kids headed to school and Emily left for work.

Before leaving, Emily called Grandpa Wilson. Carter still did not have a phone and leaving Carter along for even ten minutes was giving Emily anxiety.

As Carter and his father made their way to the hospital for outpatient physical therapy, it was the first time in a while that the two were together alone.

Despite the pride Grandpa Wilson had for Carter, the accident served as an indication of the fragility that success has and a reminder of the true priorities everyone should have.

"You probably don't want to hear this, but I feel like this accident had to happen to allow all of us to reset."

"I get it." Carter breathed deeply and watched the telephone poles roll by for a bit.

"Dad, did you ever have moments where you felt like you were missing things when I was growing up?"

"Of course. It's a natural feeling."

Carter grabbed the handle above the window and yawned as the car came to a stop at the red light.

Carter looked over to his father. "James and Amelia are growing up quickly. Even with the little extra time I've spent with them these past few days, they did things that amazed me."

"You and Emily are definitely doing something right with those kids."

The car pulled into the drop-off area for the hospital. Two familiar faces were waiting outside, John and Alexandra.

"What's happening my man?" John said as Carter approached on his crutches. "How is life outside of the hospital?"

Pretending to ignore John, Carter responded. "Alexandra! So nice to see you. I have to go see that punk, John."

Alexandra smacked John on the shoulder and chuckled.

"Oh my gosh, John. I didn't see you there."

John gave Alexandra a quick kiss and shook Carter's hand and guided him through the outpatient entrance and into the physical therapy area.

"John, awesome to see you."

"For sure, Carter. You can come straight back with me."

John pointed to the second table alongside a high school athlete who was icing what looked like an ankle injury.

Carter made his way onto the table and unstrapped the boot. John removed the bandages and checked the healing.

Grimacing through the pain of leg hair being pulled, Carter asked,

"So, what's the latest with you and Alex? I am seeing Randall this weekend and I am sure he will ask."

"She's a really sweet girl. Things are going how I think we both want them to. Thanksgiving is coming up and she invited me to join her at her sister's house for dessert. It's near my parents so I plan to swing by."

Carter was happy to hear the update and respected not prying much further. "So, I got another session in three days, what would you like me to do between then and now?"

John appreciated Carter's desire to follow his instructions and guidance.

"Listen, man, you are on the right path right now. Just stick with the exercises I gave you and add just the first one we did today. DO NOT push too hard at this point."

"Yes sir! Understood, thanks again and see you soon." Carter exited the therapy area and made his way into the waiting room where his father was sitting.

His father had the local paper open to the crossword as he looked up and saw Carter. As Carter's father stood up, he put the newspaper on the side table and threw on his coat. Carter's father then grabbed a frame from the table. Expecting to see some waiting room rules, Carter's dad showed the framed content to Carter.

"Based on our chat on the way here I thought this 'Yellow Lights for Progress' would be relevant."

"Let me see that," Carter said smiling, inspecting the enhanced version of what he gave to Doctor Z.

At the bottom of the framed principles 'Credit to one of our own Upstate Medical Patients.'

On the drive home, Carter slightly reclined the seat looking out the window most of the drive.

He knew the next few days would continue to be instrumental in his healing. Once home and with a few hours before Emily and the kids would arrive, Carter turned to his journal and expressed feelings about decisions he would face in the weeks ahead.

Twenty-Three

· · ● · ● · ● · ·

THE FOLLOWING SATURDAY WAS full of family time. Carter spent the morning in the basement playing board games with James and Amelia. After half a game of Candy Land and Amelia losing her patience, James pulled out his bin of Legos.

"Amelia, can you find a blue one with six dots?" Carter asked as they dug through the bin.

James had joined a Lego club that met once a week before school and was interested in creating structures. "So, Daddy, you always have to remember that for structures, start by looking at the foundation. If the foundation is strong and stable, you can build up and add to the sides more."

After about twenty levels of Legos were stacked, Amelia, in typical toddler fashion, swung her hand and toppled James' work over. James let out a loud dinosaur roar and Carter spent some time getting Amelia to eventually apologize.

After getting the final piece from under the couch, Carter turned to his kids, "Hey guys, let's work together this time. Remember what you said James, the foundation is important. Sometimes all of the pieces are right in front of you and it's just a matter of putting them all together to build something even greater than what your initial vision was."

It had been months since Carter had spent this level of quality time with the kids.

"Can we ask Mommy to take a picture of us and the new tower? I can put it on my desk at work."

"Can my doll be in the picture too?" Amelia asked as she giggled, sliding under Carter's arm for a big hug.

After the photoshoot by Emily, Carter told James and Amelia about the plans to go to a diner with Randall the next morning.

"Mr. Randall, that likes Skittles?" Amelia asked.

"Yep. That one."

Sunday morning came and Carter got a call from Randall around 6:30 a.m. to confirm they were still on for breakfast. Randall mentioned R.J. would be joining as well.

Emily got the kids bundled up and they hopped into the S.U.V. to head a few towns over to the diner.

Carter already knew Randall was going to make the recommendation of Mickey Mouse pancakes for the kids. Randall even admitted that just a few months before the hospital stay, he ordered the Mickey Mouse special himself.

The Wilsons arrived at the Clearview Diner around 10:00 a.m. The parking lot was packed and Carter's temporary handicapped tag helped the family get a spot close to the entrance.

As Carter stepped out of the car, a voice yelled, "Mr. Wilson, can I help you guys with anything?" It was R.J. standing with the diner door ajar.

"We are all set. Be there in a few." Carter yelled back, steadying the first crutch to the ground.

Emily held Amelia and grabbed James by the hand as they crossed the parking lot and Carter shuffled along with his crutches and boot. Emily had purchased Carter some new boot-cut pants from Target that kept Carter's leg covered and kept the gym shorts look at home.

The diner had a sign in the window: Serving the community since 1956.

As they entered, R.J. stood by the counter. The counter was full of older folks watching the news and reading papers.

"Hey Guys," R.J. said, bending down to give James and Amelia high fives. R.J. then shook Carter's hand and hugged Emily. "We just got here and my dad is at a table in the back."

R.J. walked the Wilsons to the back.

It was clear R.J. had spent a lot of time at the diner growing up based on the older waitress hugging him as they continued to the table where Randall was waiting.

Randall's back was to the Wilsons approaching the three two-top tables that had been pushed together along the back wall.

Emily slid in on the booth side, with James and Amelia following behind. Randall was wearing an army green turtleneck. Randall stood up, grasping the table as Emily and the kids joined at the table. R.J. offered Carter to sit next to Randall. As the group exchanged hellos, Emily took some crayons and coloring books out for the kids as R.J. grabbed some and started coloring with Amelia.

Randall looked over to Carter. "You are looking good."

"You too Randall"

"I won't spoil the news but R.J. took the job and starts at M.E.Z. in a few weeks."

R.J. overheard the comment and shifted from coloring. "Pops, what'd you mention about M.E.Z.?"

Carter broke in, "He mentioned you took the job. He's just a proud dad. That's awesome! In today's world, to land such a good job right out of school is no easy task. Do you have any questions for me about life there?"

Now turning full attention to Carter and his father, R.J. put down the crayons.

"Honestly, I get the sense that the goal of creating this department is to change what life is like there. At least that is what the executive team mentioned when I visited. They seem to have a good senior internal candidate they want to spearhead the transformation."

Carter repositioned himself in his seat. "Yeah. Definitely lots of room to improve but the foundation that has been built is one that can serve as a great starting point."

R.J. nodded as Carter continued, "I am actually going to drop by the office next week to meet with IT. My phone was destroyed in the crash and Emily thankfully denied me getting a new device until I was out of the hospital."

Emily was making sure the kids' juice cups were out of range for easy spills as they continued scribbling on the coloring sheets.

As the Mickey Mouse pancakes arrived, James requested his second orange juice.

As they wrapped up breakfast, R.J. stepped away from the table to take a call. It had been a while since R.J. had been in his hometown and he was adjusting to knowing the job at M.E.Z. would mean some of the memories of his mother that he tried to hide for years while away at school would certainly be resurfacing.

TWENTY-FOUR

· · · · · ● · ● · · ·

ON MONDAY, CARTER HELPED Emily through the morning routine with the kids, and while struggling to find a second shoe for Amelia, Emily got a call from Grandpa Wilson.

Grandpa Wilson was planning to be the chauffeur for Carter's physical therapy appointment and was still able to but there would be a shift in timing.

"Emily, my dad has to go into the city for bloodwork. I'm going to have him drop me at the office while he's there."

With a tense tone, Emily asked, "Why would you go into the office? Why don't you just go to the appointment with your dad."

"I don't need to, it's just a check-up on his blood pressure."

Carter continued. "I just figured we could save a trip for us and I could get set up with my new phone so you aren't continuously worrying about me when I am here alone."

Emily checked the clock and knew she had to hit the road. "Listen, I don't love the idea of you getting connected back to work when you are technically still on medical leave. Don't make me sue them by being an idiot and getting all the apps downloaded on the phone."

Carter looked at Emily. "I promise you I won't."

Hesitant, Emily kissed Carter and left through the garage door.

Carter sat on the couch for a few hours before his father arrived. At Randall's recommendation, Carter watched the first episode of the Netflix show raved about over breakfast the past weekend.

Carter's father rang the doorbell and used the spare key under the flower pot to enter the home. Carter grabbed the crutches resting on the side of the couch, his father provided a hand getting up.

"Dad, thanks for all the help these past few weeks."

"That's what family is for."

With a pat on the back, Carter led the way out the front door and into his father's car.

The morning commute was over and the roads were pretty clear. As the car stopped at the first light, Carter noticed a roadside cross. Carter closed his eyes and let out a deep breath.

Looking over at his son, Carter's father asked, "Carter, everything all right?"

Pinching his fingers over the bridge of his nose, Carter opened his eyes. "Yeah. Just finding myself processing things differently after the accident."

"I imagine that will continue for some time." Carter's father said as the light turned green.

"I hope so," Carter replied as they took the onramp where his accident had happened.

About twenty minutes later, the car approached Carter's office. There was no parking in front, only a bus lane for the city bus.

Carter's father hit the hazard lights above the radio and put the car in park. Carter's crutches had been put in the backseat, so his father stepped out of the car and helped Carter get all set on the city sidewalk.

"I will plan to be back in forty-five minutes to an hour. Will you be okay getting in?"

"Yeah, Dad. Good luck with the appointment."

Carter turned and used the crutches to get to the front door of the office lobby. Looking over his shoulder, Carter saw his father still standing on the sidewalk. A lobby attendant noticed Carter outside and approached the side door next to the main revolving door entrance.

The lobby attendant opened the door, "Let me help you."

"Thanks," Carter replied looking up.

"Are you here to see someone?"

"No, no. I work here for M.E.Z." Carter approached the entrance to the center elevator bay. Leaning against the security barrier, Carter reached into his pocket and grabbed his wallet and security card. Carter placed the card to the gate. He then realized with the crutches it wasn't going to be easy to get through. Rather than attempt to be a hero, Carter called over to the lobby attendant. "Are you able to help me open this handicap entrance?"

"Absolutely!" The young female lobby attendant typed a code into the handicapped gate. And if you will need to use this in the future, I can work with Richie to get your keycard programmed differently."

Nodding slightly, Carter felt a little embarrassed. "I appreciate that. I will ask him when I get up there."

As the elevator doors opened on Carter's floor, he was met by the M. E.Z. logo and a small reception area. Richie was at the desk. Looking up, his eyes popped out of his head as he saw Carter.

Shuffling his chair backward and standing up, Richie around the desk and hugged Carter. Richie was an early employee of M.E.Z. whom Carter was always an advocate for.

Richie stepped back. "What the hell are you doing here? How are you? I thought you weren't expected to be back for a little while."

Carter smiled. "Yeah, I'm not coming back for a while. Just was in the area and figured I would get squared away with my phone."

"I was wondering why you didn't answer my texts about the Giants game. Did you break it in the crash?"

"Yeah. It was one of the biggest blessings. Now with Emily back at work, she wanted to make sure I had something so she could stay in touch."

Richie had returned behind his desk. "Sit down right there and I can call I.T. to let them know you are here."

Carter leaned forward in the chair, looking down from the reception area to the main floor space. After Richie placed the call to I.T., an inbound call came in, so it was a few minutes before Richie freed up.

Richie looked up towards Carter. "Sorry about that. I.T. is wrapping up a meeting. Someone will be up in a few minutes."

Normally Carter trekked the floor like he owned it. Today, he sat in the yellow reception chairs patiently.

The I.T. Manager entered through the elevator bay. I.T. sat one floor down.

"Carter! I was surprised to hear you were here. Richie mentioned you want to get your phone set up?"

"Yeah, if you could, that would be great. My wife doesn't like that she can't reach me while I am home alone."

The I.T. Manager was already holding a spare phone in his hand. "Got it. How long do you got?"

"About thirty minutes. I am sorry. I should have called ahead. If you can't do it, that's fine." Carter replied. Carter tended to be known to make fire-drill requests in the past.

Sensing the thirty minutes would be tight, Carter added, "If it helps, my wife doesn't want any of the work apps downloaded until I am actually back."

The I.T. Manager laughed. "That makes this way more manageable in thirty minutes. I assume you want the same number you had before?"

"If that's possible," Carter replied.

"It is. I got about fifteen minutes now. I just need to register this device into our device inventory and do a few setting adjustments. Will you just be hanging here?"

Carter's jaw was hanging at how simple the I.T. Manager made the phone activation process sound. "I might swing down to see Jeff."

"Okay. I will drop it off with Richie once I am done and if you aren't here."

The I.T. Manager headed back down as Richie checked the calendar of Jeff, Carter's boss.

Richie looked up from his computer monitors. "It looks like Jeff has a meeting in fifteen minutes. Let me call down to see if he's there. I don't want you to push yourself too much moving around."

Sitting patiently, Carter listened to Richie and was signaled with a thumbs up and a point toward Jeff's office.

Bracing the side of the comfy reception area chairs, Carter stood up putting pressure on his good leg and setting the crutches in place. As Carter began down the hallway, he saw Jeff come out of his office waving and with a smile.

Carter passed an area of cubicles with members of his team. There were helium balloons spelling 'Congrats!' flowing from one side of the team's area to the other.

Only about ten feet ahead, Jeff shouted. "Carter! Last night the team won the Chambers account."

Semi-frustrated he had no way to be informed and through the roof knowing what it meant to M.E.Z. Carter smiled. "YES! Great job everyone."

Many of the team members looked over their cubicles and turned their chairs at the commotion and Carter's reply.

A mix of smiles from the team and some uneasiness from others at seeing Carter back.

Jeff and Carter continued to the corner office and Jeff closed the door. Rather than sit down, Carter remained standing with his crutches as Jeff picked up his phone to double-check the time.

Jeff patted Carter on the shoulder. "How are you doing? Emily called me a few days after the accident but I knew it was best to give you space."

Carter put his lips together and nodded before replying. "Honestly, this accident was horrific and a setback in some ways but I think an accelerant for a better future for myself, my family, and my ability to help others."

Jeff nodded. "You probably also loved that the phone broke and I couldn't track you down?"

Laughing, Carter replied. "If we had a home phone still, I probably would have waited until my official day back before coming in. Just so you know, I.T. isn't putting any of the work apps on my phone."

Eyebrow scrunched and a bit confused, Jeff started to reply. "Listen, Carter. I wanted to bring you in here for a few reasons. You were burning the stick at both ends before this accident and the board was going to make me force you to take time. I want you to take the remainder of the year."

Not sure what emotion was appropriate in hearing that news, Carter stood silently. After thirty seconds, Carter jumped in. "I was such a big piece of getting the Chambers account across. You aren't thinking of firing me, are you?"

Jeff looked up. "Hahaha, Jesus, Carter. That's far from what we are thinking. I have this call in six minutes. Number one, H.R. was planning to call you tomorrow anyway saying to remain on leave through year-end. Number two, I want to put a new role in front of you for consideration."

Carter wished he had been sitting down, as the weight of the discussion and route the conversation was heading was mentally straining. Almost as straining as the physical pain of standing with crutches.

"Last board meeting, we talked about the Transformation Office we are building out as we continue to grow. While you were out, we found a super-skilled candidate who will be joining us in the New Year. He's going to be fantastic and the board began thinking about the future leaders of M.E.Z. who could lead that department." There was a nod in Carter's direction.

Carter smirked, curious if R.J. was the candidate being referenced. "And you think I could be the one to lead it?"

Jeff looked Carter straight in the eyes. "I know you can do it and some of the comments you made today reassure me that you are the right person."

Getting a notification on his computer, Jeff stood up. "I need to hop on this call. Do you think you can let me know by this time next week if you want me to have them hold off on an outside search and have you start the Chief Transformation Officer on January 2nd?"

Jeff clicked on the meeting link. "Hey Chambers Team. Carter swung by the office and is standing with me."

There were hellos, how are yous, oh my goshs from the other side. Carter was still processing the offer Jeff made seconds before.

Carter replied from the other side of the desk. "Hi all! I was excited to hear the news about the expanded partnership. I just dropped by today and will be returning after the holidays."

Carter turned and left Jeff's office nodding his head slightly.

As Carter passed by the team on the main floor, he called out. "Congrats again on the Chambers win!"

Some of the folks on the floor were also on the same call as Jeff and simply shared a thumbs-up.

As Carter approached the reception area, his new phone was sitting on the desk and Richie was on a call. A large clock was set above where Richie was sitting. Carter's father wouldn't be outside for a few minutes.

Richie hung up. "How'd it go with Jeff?"

Carter smiled and reached into his pocket. Carter pulled out his wallet, unfolded a piece of paper, and placed it on the desk.

"Richie, it went great. I have a lot to think about. Let's just say the transformation I am going through from this injury could be just the beginning."

Richie grabbed the unfolded paper. "What is this?"

Carter's smile glowed. "This will shape the principles of M.E.Z. for years to come. I'm going to leave it with you. Can you make copies for the team and hand them out?"

Printed in Great Britain
by Amazon

26228499R00079